Revise
A2

Physics

Graham Booth & David Brodie

Contents

Chapter 3 Thermal and particle physics

Chapter 4 Further physics

Chapter 5 Synthesis and How Science Works

AS/A2 Level Physics courses

AS and A2

All Physics A Level courses are in two parts, with three separate units or modules in each part. Most students will start by studying the AS (Advanced Subsidiary) course. Some will then go on to study the second part of the A Level course, called the A2. It is also possible to study the full A Level course, both AS and A2, in any order.

How will you be tested?

Assessment units

For AS Physics, assessment is in three units. For the full A Level, you will take a further three units that make up A2 Physics. AS Physics forms 50% of the assessment weighting for the full A Level.

Units that are assessed by written examination can normally be taken in either January or June. Coursework units can be completed for assessment only in June. It is also possible to study the whole course before taking any of the unit tests. There is a lot of flexibility about when exams can be taken and the diagram below shows just some of the ways that the assessment units may be taken for AS and A Level Physics.

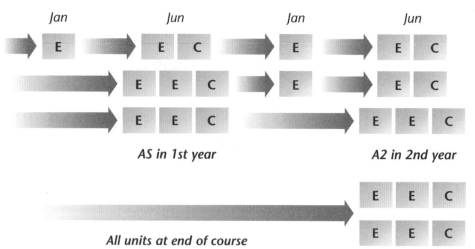

If you are disappointed with a unit result then you can re-sit the unit examination. The higher mark counts.

External assessment

For external assessment, written examinations are set and marked by teachers and lecturers from across the country, and overseen by the awarding bodies.

Internal assessment

Internal assessment is based on work that you do over a period of time, and is marked by your own teachers or lecturers. Some or all of your internally assessed work is based on practical and investigative skills and communication of your work.

Synoptic assessment

Some questions will require you to make and use connections within and between different areas of physics. They require a 'synoptic' or 'overview' approach. So, for example, you could be asked to compare energy storage by different systems such as stretched springs and charged capacitors, or to recognise and distinguish patterns in relationships such as those dealing with different kinds of rate of change.

What will you need to be able to do?

You will be tested by 'assessment objectives'. These are the skills and abilities that you should have acquired by studying the course. The assessment objectives for A2 Physics are shown below.

Knowledge and understanding of science and How Science Works

- recognising, recalling and showing understanding of scientific knowledge
- selection, organisation and communication of relevant information in a variety of forms.

Application of knowledge and understanding of science and How Science Works

- analysis and evaluation scientific knowledge and processes
- applying scientific knowledge and processes to unfamiliar situations including those related to issues
- assessing the validity, reliability and credibility of scientific information.

How Science Works

- demonstrating and describing ethical, safe and skilful practical techniques and processes
- selecting appropriate qualitative and quantitative methods
- making, recording and communicating reliable and valid observations and measurements with appropriate precision and accuracy
- analysis, interpretation, explanation and evaluation of the methodology, results and impact of their own and others' experimental and investigative activities in a variety of ways.

The awarding bodies and their specifications

The awarding bodies in England, Wales and Northern Ireland are AQA, CCEA, Edexcel, OCR and WJEC/CBAC. These awarding bodies oversee the development of specifications and examinations as well as marking and moderation.

AQA A Physics

ASSESSMENT UNIT	TOPIC, SECTION OR MODULE	CHAPTER REFERENCE	STUDIED	REVISED	PRACTICE QUESTIONS
4. Fields and Further Mechanics	Further Mechanics	1.2, 1.3, 1.4, 1.5, 2.5			
	Gravitation	2.1, 2.5			
	Electric Fields	2.2			
	Capacitance	2.3			
	Magnetic Fields	2.4, 2.5, 2.6			
5. Nuclear Physics, Thermal Physics and an Optional Topic	Radioactivity	3.3			
	Nuclear Energy	3.4			
	Thermal Physics	3.1, 3.2			
	Options: • Astrophysics • Medical Physics • Applied Physics • Turning points in Physics	4.3, 4.4 4.1, 4.2 3.1, 3.2 1.6			
6. Investigative and Practical Skills, Internally assessed					

A2 assessment analysis

Unit 4	1 h 45 min test	40%
Unit 5	1 h 45 min test	40%
Unit 6	Internally assessed practical skills and investigative skills	20%

AQA B Physics

ASSESSMENT UNIT	TOPIC, SECTION OR MODULE	CHAPTER REFERENCE	STUDIED	REVISED	PRACTICE QUESTIONS
4. Physics inside out	Experiences out of this world	1.1, 1.2, 2.1, 3.2			
	What goes around comes around	1.3, 1.4, 1.5, 4.6			
	Imaging the invisible	2.1, 2.6, 3.6, 4.2			
2. Energy Under the Microscope	Matter Under the Microscope	3.1, 3.2			
	Breaking Matter Down	2.2, 2.4, 2.5, 3.5			
	Energy from the Nucleus	3.3, 3.4, 3.5			
4. Investigative and Practical Skills, Internally assessed					

A2 assessment analysis

Unit 1	1 h 45 min test	40%
Unit 2	1 h 45 min test	40%
Unit 3	Internally assessed practical skills and investigative skills	20%

CCEA Physics

ASSESSMENT UNIT	TOPIC, SECTION OR MODULE	CHAPTER REFERENCE	STUDIED	REVISED	PRACTICE QUESTIONS
1. Momentum, Thermal Physics, Circular Motion, Oscillations and Atomic and Nuclear Physics	Mechanics (momentum, circular motion, simple harmonic motion)	1.1, 1.2, 1.3, 1.4, 1.5			
	Thermal Physics	3.1, 3.2			
	The Nucleus	3.3, 3.4, 3.5			
2. Fields and their Applications	Gravitational Fields	2.1			
	Electric Fields and Capacitors	2.2, 2.3			
	Magnetic Fields	2.4, 2.5			
	Particles	3.5, 3.6			
3. Practical Techniques					

A2 assessment analysis

Unit 1	1 h 30 min test	37%
Unit 2	1 h 30 min test	37%
Unit 3	Internally assessed practical techniques	26%

Edexcel Physics, concept approach

ASSESSMENT UNIT	TOPIC, SECTION OR MODULE	CHAPTER REFERENCE	STUDIED	REVISED	PRACTICE QUESTIONS
4. Physics on the Move	Further Mechanics	1.1, 1.2, 1.3			
	Electric and Magnetic Fields	2.2, 2.3, 2.4, 2.6			
	Particle Physics	2.5, 3.5, 3.6, 3.7			
5. Physics from Creation to Collapse	Thermal Energy	3.1, 3.2			
	Nuclear Decay	3.3			
	Oscillations	1.4, 1.5			
	Astrophysics and Cosmology	3.4, 4.3, 4.4			
6. Experimental Physics					

A2 assessment analysis

Unit 1	1 h 35 min test	40%
Unit 2	1 h 35 min test	40%
Unit 3	Internally assessed practical experiment	20%

Edexcel Physics, context approach

ASSESSMENT UNIT	TOPIC, SECTION OR MODULE	CHAPTER REFERENCE	STUDIED	REVISED	PRACTICE QUESTIONS
4. Physics on the Move	Transport on Track	1.2, 2.3, 2.4, 2.6			
	The Medium is the Message	2.2, 2.3, 2.4, 2.5			
	Probing the Heart of Matter	1.1, 1.2, 1.3, 2.2, 2.5, 3.5, 3.6, 3.7			
5. Physics from Creation to Collapse	Reach for the Stars	2.1, 3.1, 3.2, 3.3, 3.4, 4.3, 4.4			
	Build or Bust?	1.5			
6. Experimental Physics					

A2 assessment analysis

Unit 1	1 h 35 min test	40%
Unit 2	1 h 35 min test	40%
Unit 3	Internally assessed practical experiment	20%

OCR Physics A

ASSESSMENT UNIT	TOPIC, SECTION OR MODULE	CHAPTER REFERENCE	STUDIED	REVISED	PRACTICE QUESTIONS
1. The Newtonian World	Newton's Laws and Momentum	1.1, 1.2			
	Circular Motion and Oscillations	1.3, 1.4, 1.5, 2.1,			
	Thermal Physics	3.1, 3.2			
2. Fields, Particles and Frontiers of Physics	Electric and Magnetic Fields	2.2, 2.4, 2.6			
	Capacitors and Exponential Decay	2.3			
	Nuclear Physics	3.3, 3.4, 3.5			
	Medical Imaging	4.2			
	Modelling the Universe	4.3, 4.4			
3. Practical Skills in Physics 2					

A2 assessment analysis

Unit 1	1 h test	*30%*
Unit 2	1 h 45 min test	*50%*
Unit 3	Internally marked practical tasks	*20%*

Both of the written papers are specified as 'synoptic', meaning that they test understanding between different aspects of Physics.

OCR Physics B

ASSESSMENT UNIT	TOPIC, SECTION OR MODULE	CHAPTER REFERENCE	STUDIED	REVISED	PRACTICE QUESTIONS
1. Rise and Fall of the Clockwork Universe	Models and Rules	1.1, 1.2, 1.4, 1.5, 2.1, 2.3, 3.3, 4.3, 4.4			
	Matter in extremes	3.1, 3.2			
2. Field and Particle Pictures	Fields	2.2, 2.4, 2.6			
	Fundamental Particles	2.5, 3.3, 3.4, 3.5, 3.6			
3. Researching Physics					

A2 assessment analysis

Unit 1	1 h 15 min test	30%
Unit 2	2 h test	50%
Unit 3	Internal assessment of practical skills	20%

WJEC/CBAC Physics

ASSESSMENT UNIT	TOPIC, SECTION OR MODULE	CHAPTER REFERENCE	STUDIED	REVISED	PRACTICE QUESTIONS
4. Oscillations and Fields	Vibrations	1.3, 1.4, 1.5			
	Momentum Concepts	1.1, 1.2			
	Thermal Physics	3.1, 3.2			
	Electrostatic and Gravitational Fields of Force	2.1, 2.2			
	Application to Orbits in the Solar System and the Wider Universe	2.1, 4.3, 4.4			
5. Electromagnetism, Nuclei and Options	Capacitance	2.3			
	B-Fields	2.4, 2.5			
	Electromagnetic Induction	2.6			
	Radioactivity and Radioisotopes	3.3, 3.4, 3.5			
	Nuclear Energy	3.4			
	Options: • Further electromagnetism and alternating current • Revolutions in Physics • Materials • Biological measurement and medical imaging • Energy matters	2.6 1.2, 1.6, 2.1, 2.2, 2.5, 2.6, 4.5 AS chapter 1 4.1, 4.2 3.1, 3.2, AS chapter 1			
3. Experimental Physics					

A2 assessment analysis

Unit 4	*1 h 15 min test*	*36%*
Unit 5	*1 h 45 min test*	*44%*
Unit 6	*Internally assessed experimental tasks*	*20%*

13

Different types of questions in A2 examinations

In A2 Level Physics unit examinations, there may be combinations of short-answer questions and structured questions requiring both short answers and more extended answers. There may be some free-response and open-ended questions. There may also be some questions with a multiple-choice or 'objective' format.

Short-answer questions

A short-answer question may test recall or it may test understanding by requiring you to undertake a short, one-stage calculation. Short-answer questions normally have space for the answers printed on the question paper. Here are some examples (the answers are shown in blue):

What is the relationship between electric current and charge flow?

Current = rate of flow of charge.

The current passing in a heater is 6 A when it operates from 240 V mains. Calculate the power of the heating element.

$P = I \times V = 6\,A \times 240\,V = 1440\,W$

Which of the following is the correct unit of acceleration?

A $m\,s^{-1}$
B $s\,m^{-1}$
C $m\,s^{-2}$
D $m^2\,s^{-1}$

C $m\,s^{-2}$

Structured questions

Structured questions are in several parts. The parts are usually about a common context and they often become progressively more difficult and more demanding as you work your way through the question. They may start with simple recall, then test understanding of a familiar or an unfamiliar situation. The most difficult part of a structured question is usually at the end, where the candidate is sometimes asked to suggest a reason for a particular phenomenon or social implication.

When answering structured questions, do not feel that you have to complete one question before starting the next. The further you are into a question, the more difficult the marks are to obtain. If you run out of ideas, go on to the next question. Five minutes spent on the beginning of that question are likely to be much more fruitful than the same time spent racking your brains trying to think of an explanation for an unfamiliar phenomenon.

Here is an example of a structured question that becomes progressively more demanding.

(a) A car speeds up from $20\,m\,s^{-1}$ to $50\,m\,s^{-1}$ in $15\,s$.

Calculate the acceleration of the car.

acceleration = increase in velocity ÷ time taken
$= 30\,m\,s^{-1} \div 15\,s = 2\,m\,s^{-2}$

(b) The total mass of the car and contents is 950 kg.

Calculate the size of the unbalanced force required to cause this acceleration.

force = mass × acceleration
     = 950 kg × 2 m s^{-2} = 1900 N

(c) Suggest why the size of the driving force acting on the car needs to be greater than the answer to (b).

The driving force also has to do work to overcome the resistive forces, e.g. air resistance and rolling resistance.

Extended answers

Questions requiring more **extended answers** will usually form part of structured questions. They will normally appear at the end of structured questions and be characterised by having at least three marks (and often more, typically five) allocated to the answers as well as several lines (up to ten) of answer space. These questions are also used to assess your abilities to communicate ideas and put together a logical argument.

The correct answers to extended questions are less well-defined than those for short-answer questions. Examiners may have a list of points for which credit is awarded up to the maximum for the question, or they may first of all judge the quality of your response as poor, satisfactory or good before allocating it a mark within a range that corresponds to that quality.

As an example of a question that requires an extended answer, a structured question on the use of solar energy could end with the following:

Suggest why very few buildings make use of solar energy in this country compared to countries in southern Europe.   [5]

Points that the examiners might look for include:

- the energy from the Sun is unreliable due to cloud cover
- the intensity of the Sun's radiation is less in this country than in southern Europe due to the Earth's curvature
- more energy is absorbed by the atmosphere as the radiation has a greater depth of atmosphere to travel through
- fossil fuels are in abundant supply and relatively cheap
- the capital cost is high, giving a long payback time
- photo-voltaic cells have a low efficiency
- the energy is difficult to store for the times when it is needed the most

Full marks would be awarded for an argument that puts forward three or four of these points in a clear and logical way.

Free-response questions

Some test papers may make use of free-response and open-ended questions. These types of questions allow you to choose the context and to develop your own ideas. Examples could include 'Describe a laboratory method of determining g, the value of free-fall acceleration' and 'Outline the evidence that suggests that light has a wave-like behaviour'. When answering these types of questions it is important to plan your response and present your answer in a logical order.

Stretch and Challenge

Stretch and Challenge is a concept that is applied to the structured questions in Units 4 and 5 of the exam papers, for A2. In principle, it means that the sub-questions become progressively harder so as to challenge more able students and help differentiate between A and A* students.

Stretch and Challenge questions are designed to test a variety of different skills and your understanding of the material. They are likely to test your ability to make appropriate connections between different areas and apply your knowledge in unfamiliar contexts (as opposed to basic recall).

Exam technique

Continuity from AS to A2

If you have already studied AS units then you will find that the work at A2 follows on, developing ideas and skills further. This book provides all of the new material for A2 Physics, and it repeats some key points of examination technique and mathematical skills. However, A2 assessment can require knowledge of AS work, so for your preparation for tests you will need to look at this book and its AS companion.

What are examiners looking for?

Examiners use instructions to help you to decide the length and depth of your answer. If a question does not seem to make sense, you may have misread it – read it again!

State, define or list

This requires a short, concise answer, often recall of material that can be learnt by rote.

Explain, describe or discuss

Some reasoning or reference to theory is required, depending on the context.

Outline

This implies a short response, almost a list of sentences or bullet points.

Predict or deduce

You are not expected to answer by recall but by making a connection between pieces of information.

Suggest

You are expected to apply your general knowledge to a 'novel' situation, one which you have not directly studied during the AS Physics course.

Calculate

This is used when a numerical answer is required. You should always use units in quantities and use significant figures with care. Look to see how many significant figures have been used for quantities in the question and give your answer to this degree of precision. If the question uses 3 (sig figs), then give your answer to 3 (sig figs) also.

Some dos and don'ts

Dos

Do answer the question

- No credit can be given for good Physics that is irrelevant to the question.

Do use the mark allocation to guide how much you write

- Two marks are awarded for two valid points – writing more will rarely gain more credit and could mean wasted time or even contradicting earlier valid points.

Do use diagrams, equations and tables in your responses

- Even in 'essay-type' questions, these offer an excellent way of communicating Physics. It is worth your while to practise drawing good clear and labelled sketches. Normally, you should do this without use of rulers or other drawing instruments.

Do write legibly

- An examiner cannot give marks if the answer cannot be read.

Do write using correct spelling and grammar. Structure longer essays carefully

- Marks are now awarded for the quality of your language in exams.

Don'ts

Don't fill up any blank space on a paper

- In structured questions, the number of dotted lines should guide the length of your answer.
- If you write too much, you waste time and may not finish the exam paper. You also risk contradicting yourself.

Don't write out the question again

- This wastes time. The marks are for the answer!

Don't contradict yourself

- The examiner cannot be expected to choose which answer is intended. You could lose a hard-earned mark.

Don't spend too much time on a part that you find difficult

- You may not have enough time to complete the exam. You can always return to a difficult calculation if you have time at the end of the exam.

What grade do you want?

Everyone would like to improve their grades but you will only manage this with a lot of hard work and determination. You should have a fair idea of your natural ability and likely grade in Physics and the hints below offer advice on improving that grade.

For a Grade E

You cannot afford to miss the easy marks. Even if you find Physics difficult to understand and would be happy with a Grade E, there are plenty of questions in which you can gain marks.

- You must memorise all definitions.
- You must practise exam questions to give yourself confidence that you do know some Physics. In exams, answer the parts of questions that you know first. You must not waste time on the difficult parts. You can always go back to these later.
- The areas of Physics that you find most difficult are going to be hard to score on in exams. Even in the difficult questions, there are still marks to be gained. Show your working in calculations because credit is given for a sound method. You can always gain some marks if you get part of the way towards the solution.

For a Grade C

You must have a reasonable grasp of Physics but you may have weaknesses in several areas and you will be unsure of some of the reasons for the Physics.

- Many Grade C candidates are just as good at answering questions as the Grade A students but holes and weaknesses often show up in just some topics.
- To improve, you will need to master your weaknesses and you must prepare thoroughly for the exam. You must become a better all-rounder.

For a Grade A

You will need to be a very good all-rounder.

- You must go into every exam knowing the work extremely well.
- You must be able to apply your knowledge to new, unfamiliar situations.
- You need to have practised many, many exam questions so that you are ready for the type of question that will appear.

The exams test all areas of the specification and any weaknesses in your Physics will be found out. There must be no holes in your knowledge and understanding. For a Grade A, you must be competent in all areas.

For a Grade A*

The Awarding bodies have now introduced an A* grade for A level. This follows on from the introduction of this grade at GCSE and is intended to be awarded to a relatively small number of the highest scoring candidates.

To achieve an A* grade you must score over 80% on all six units combined (grade A) but also **90%** on the three **A2 units** combined. This is quite a difficult target!

What marks do you need?

The table below shows how your average mark is transferred into a grade.

average	80%	70%	60%	50%	40%
grade	A	B	C	D	E

Essential mathematics

This section describes some of the mathematical techniques that are needed in studying AS Level Physics.

Quantities and units

Physical quantities are described by the appropriate words or symbols, for example the symbol R is used as shorthand for the value of a *resistance*. The quantity that the word or symbol represents has both a numerical value and a unit, e.g. 10.5 Ω. When writing data in a table or plotting a graph, only the numerical values are entered or plotted. For this reason headings used in tables and labels on graph axes are always written as (physical quantity)/(unit), where the slash represents division. When a physical quantity is divided by its unit, the result is the numerical value of the quantity.

Resistance is an example of a **derived** quantity and the ohm is a derived unit. This means that they are defined in terms of other quantities and units. All derived quantities and units can be expressed in terms of the seven **base** quantities and units of the SI, or International System of Units.

The quantities, their units and symbols are shown in the table. The candela is not used in AS or A2 Level Physics.

Quantity	Unit	Symbol
length	metre	m
mass	kilogram	kg
time	second	s
electric current	ampere	A
temperature difference	kelvin	K
amount of substance	mole	mol
luminous intensity	candela	cd

Equations

Physical quantities and homogeneous equations

The equations that you use in Physics are relationships between physical quantities. The value of a physical quantity includes both the numerical value and the unit it is measured in.

An equation must be **homogeneous**. That is, the units on each side of the equation must be the same.

For example, the equation:

    4 cats + 5 dogs = 9 camels

is nonsense because it is not homogeneous.

Likewise:

    4 A + 5 V = 9 Ω

is not homogeneous, and makes no sense.

However, the equations:

    4 cats + 5 cats = 9 cats

and:

    4 A + 5 A = 9 A

are homogeneous and correct.

Checking homogeneity in an equation is useful for:

• finding the units of a constant such as resistivity

- checking the possible correctness of an equation; if the units on each side are the same, the equation may be correct, but if they are different it is definitely wrong.

When to include units after values

A physicist will often write the equation:

$$4A \quad + \quad 5A \quad = \quad 9A$$

as:

$$4 \quad + \quad 5 \quad = \quad 9$$
$$\text{total current} \quad = \quad 9A$$

That is, it is permissible to leave out the unit in working, providing that the unit is given with the answer.

The equals sign

The = sign is at the heart of Mathematics, and it is a good habit never to use it incorrectly. In Physics especially, **the = sign is telling us that the two quantities either side are physically identical.** They may not look the same in the equation, but in the observable world we would not be able to tell the difference between one and the other. We cannot, for example, tell the difference between (4 + 5) cats and 9 cats however long we stare at them. This is a rule that is so obvious that people often forget it.

We can tell the difference between (4 + 5 + 1) cats and 9 cats (if they keep still for long enough).

(4 + 5 + 1) cats ≠ 9 cats

The ≠ sign means **not** equal. An equals sign in this 'equation' would not be telling the truth.

We cannot tell the difference between (4 + 5 + 1) cats and (9 + 1) cats.

(4 + 5 + 1) cats = (9 + 1) cats

The equals sign is telling the truth.

This reveals another rule that is also quite simple, but people often find it hard because they forget that = signs can only ever be used to tell the truth about indistinguishability. The new rule is that **you cannot change one side of an equation without changing the other in the same way.**

Rearranging equations

Often equations need to be used in a different form from that in which they are given or remembered. The equation needs to be rearranged. The rules for rearranging are:

- both sides of the equation must be changed in exactly the same way
- add and subtract before multiplying and dividing, and finally deal with roots and powers.

For example, suppose that you know the equation $v^2 = u^2 + 2as$ (and you know that the = sign here is telling the truth), and you want to work out u.

First, subtract 2as from both sides.

$$v^2 - 2as = u^2$$

(Check that you feel happy that this = sign is being honest. It will be if you have done the same thing to both sides of the original equation.)

Second, 'square root' both sides of the equation.

$$\sqrt{(v^2 - 2as)} = u$$

The hard part is not changing the equation (provided you remember the rules) but knowing what changes to make to get from the original form to the one you want.

It's not rocket science, but it does take practice.

For simple equations such as V = IR there is an alternative method, using the 'magic triangle'.

Write the equation in to the triangle. Cover up the quantity you want to work out. The pattern in the triangle tells you the equation you want.

The alternative method is to apply the rules as above, and change both sides of the equation in the same way. So if you divide both sides by R, you get V/R = I.

For equations such as these, it makes sense to use whichever method works best for you.

Drawing graphs

Graphs have a number of uses in Physics:

- they give an immediate, visual display of the relationship between physical quantities
- they enable the values of quantities to be determined
- they can be used to support or disprove a hypothesis about the relationship between variables.

When plotting a graph, it is important to remember that values determined by experiment are not exact. Every measurement has a certain level of accuracy and a certain level of precision.

An accurate measurement is one that agrees with the 'true' value. (Of course, the only way to find out a value of a physical quantity is to measure it, or to calculate it from other measured values. So the 'true' value is an ideal, and may be impossible to know.)

A precise measurement is one that agrees closely with repeated measurements. Precise measurements generally allow values to be given with confidence to more decimal places.

Perfect accuracy and perfect precision are fundamentally impossible. For these reasons, having plotted experimental values on a grid, the graph line is drawn as the best straight line or smooth curve that represents the points. Where there are 'anomalous' results, i.e. points that do not fit the straight line or curve, these should always be checked. If in doubt, ignore them, but do add a note in your experimental work to explain why you have ignored them and suggest how any anomalous results could have arisen.

Graphs, gradients and rates of change

Quantities such as velocity, acceleration and power are defined in terms of a **rate of change** of another quantity with time. This rate of change can be determined by calculating the gradient of an appropriate graph. For example, *velocity* is the *rate of change of displacement with time*. Its value is represented by the gradient of a displacement–time graph. Different techniques are used to determine the gradient of a straight line and a smooth curve. For a straight line:

- determine the value of Δy, the change in the value of the quantity plotted on the y-axis, using the whole of the straight line part of the graph

A common error when determining the gradient of a graph is to work it out using the gridlines only, without reference to the scales on each axis.

- determine the corresponding value of Δx
- calculate the gradient as $\Delta y \div \Delta x$

For a smooth curve, the gradient is calculated by first drawing a tangent to the curve and then using the above method to determine the gradient of the tangent. To draw a tangent to a curve:

- mark the point on the curve where the gradient is to be determined
- use a pair of compasses to mark in two points on the curve, close to and equidistant from the point where the gradient is to be determined
- join these points with a ruler and extend the line beyond each point.

These techniques are illustrated in the diagrams below.

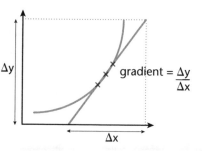

This calculation provides the value of the gradient of the middle section of the graph only. The other two sections have different gradients.

This method provides the value of the gradient at the middle of the three red marks. The graph has a continuously changing gradient that starts small and increases.

The area under a curve

The area between a graph line and the horizontal axis, often referred to as the 'area under the graph' can also yield useful information. This is the case when the product of the quantities plotted on the axes represents another physical quantity.

For example, on a *speed–time* graph this area represents the distance travelled. In the case of a straight line, the area can be calculated as that of the appropriate geometric figure. Where the graph line is curved, then the method of 'counting squares' is used.

- Count the number of complete squares between the graph line and the horizontal axis.

- Fractions of squares are counted as '1' if half the square or more is under the line, otherwise '0'.

- To work out the physical significance of each square, multiply together the quantities represented by one grid division on each axis.

These techniques are illustrated in the diagrams below:

Equations from graphs

By plotting the values of two variable quantities on a suitable graph, it may be possible to determine the relationship between the variables. This is straightforward when the graph is a straight line, since all straight line graphs have an equation of the form $y = mx + c$, where m is the gradient of the graph and c is the value of y when x is zero, i.e. the intercept on the y-axis. The relationship between the variables is determined by finding the values of m and c.

The straight line graph on the left shows how the displacement, s, of an object varies with time, t.

The equation that describes this motion is:

$s = 0.016t - 0.14$

(Note that no units are shown in the equation, for simplicity. The unit for displacement, s, is the metre and the unit for time, t, is the second. The physical value 0.016 has unit metre per second, and the physical value 0.14 is measured in metres.)

There is an important and special case of the equation $y = mx + c$. This is the case for which c is zero, so that $y = mx$. The straight line of this graph now passes through the graph's origin.

m is the gradient of the graph and is constant (since the graph is a single straight line). Note that different symbols can be used for the constant gradient in place of m. It is quite common, for example, to use k. That gives $y = kx$.

In Physics, we are often seeking simple patterns, and this is about as simple as patterns can be. If $y = mx$ or $y = kx$, whatever changes happen to x then y always changes by the same proportion.

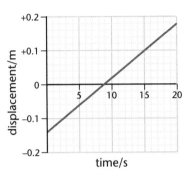

gradient = 0.32 ÷ 20
 = 0.016 m s^{-1}
intercept on y-axis = –0.14

equation is s = 0.016t – 0.14

Trigonometry and Pythagoras

In the right-angled triangle shown here, the sides are labelled o (opposite), a (adjacent) and h (hypotenuse). The relationships between the size of the angle θ and the lengths of these sides are shown on the left.

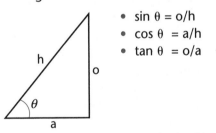

- $\sin \theta = o/h$
- $\cos \theta = a/h$
- $\tan \theta = o/a$

Pythagoras' theorem gives the relationship between the sides of a right-angled triangle: $h^2 = a^2 + o^2$

Multiples

For A2 Level Physics, you are expected to be familiar with the following multiples of units:

Name	Multiple	Symbol
pico-	10^{-12}	p
nano-	10^{-9}	n
micro-	10^{-6}	μ
milli-	10^{-3}	m
kilo-	10^{3}	k
mega-	10^{6}	M
giga-	10^{9}	G

For example, the symbol MHz means 1×10^6 Hz and mN means 1×10^{-3} N.

Four steps to successful revision

Step 1: Understand

- Mark up the text if necessary – underline, highlight and make notes.
- Re-read each paragraph slowly.

GO TO STEP 2

Step 2: Summarise

- Now make your own revision note summary:
  What is the main idea, theme or concept to be learnt?
  What are the main points? How does the logic develop?
  Ask questions: Why? How? What next?
- Use bullet points, mind maps, patterned notes.
- Link ideas with mnemonics, mind maps, crazy stories.
- Note the title and date of the revision notes
  (e.g. Physics: Electricity, 3rd March).
- Organise your notes carefully and keep them in a file.

This is now in **short-term memory**. You will forget 80% of it if you do not go to Step 3.
GO TO STEP 3, but first take a 10 minute break.

Step 3: Memorise

- Take 25 minute learning 'bites' with 5 minute breaks.
- After each 5 minute break test yourself:
  Cover the original revision note summary
  Write down the main points
  Speak out loud (record on tape)
  Tell someone else
  Repeat many times.

The material is well on its way to **long-term memory**.
You will forget 40% if you do not do Step 4. **GO TO STEP 4**

Step 4: Track/Review

- Create a Revision Diary (one A4 page per day).
- Make a revision plan for the topic, e.g. 1 day later, 1 week later,
  1 month later.
- Record your revision in your Revision Diary, e.g.
  Physics: Electricity, 3rd March 25 minutes
  Physics: Electricity, 5th March 15 minutes
  Physics: Electricity, 3rd April 15 minutes
  ... revisit each topic at monthly intervals.

Chapter 1

Mechanics

The following topics are covered in this chapter:

- *Newton I and III*
- *Momentum and the second law*
- *Motion in a circle*

- *Oscillations, resonance and damping*
- *Simple harmonic motion*
- *Relativity*

1.1 Newton I and III

After studying this section you should be able to:

- *state Newton's first and third laws of motion*
- *apply the first law to situations where the forces acting on an object are balanced and unbalanced*
- *apply the third law to the forces acting on two objects that interact*

LEARNING SUMMARY

Newton's laws of motion

With his three laws of motion, Newton aimed to describe and predict the movement of every object in the Universe. Like many other 'laws' in physics, they give the right answers much of the time. The paths of planets, moons and satellites are all worked out using Newton's laws.

This section looks at formal statements of the first and third law and how they apply to everyday situations.

The first law

AQA B	4
OCR A	G484

> **KEY POINT**
>
> Newton's first law states that:
> An object maintains its state of rest or uniform motion unless there is a resultant, or unbalanced, force acting on it.

> The phrase 'uniform motion' means moving in a straight line at constant speed, i.e. moving at constant velocity.

friction and air resistance create a resultant force on this sliding object

At first, this seems contrary to everyday experience. Give an object a push and it slows down before coming to rest. This is not 'continuing in a state of uniform motion'. Newton realised that in this case the unseen **resistive forces** of **friction** and **air resistance** together act in opposition to the motion; as there is no longer a driving force after the object has been pushed, there is a resultant backwards-directed force acting on it.

> **Key point from AS**
>
> - **When the forces on an object are balanced, the vector diagram is a closed figure.**
> *Revise AS section 1.1*

Motion without resistive forces is difficult to achieve on Earth. There is always air resistance or friction from a surface that a moving object rests on. The nearest that we can get to modelling motion with no resistive forces is to study motion on ice or an air track.

The converse of Newton's first law is also true:

> if an object is at rest or moving at constant velocity the resultant force on it is zero

This means that where there are two forces acting on an object that satisfies these conditions, they must be equal in size and opposite in direction. If there are three or more forces acting then the vector diagram is a closed figure.

One example of the first law is a vehicle moving at constant velocity; the **driving force** and **resistive force** are equal in size and act in opposite directions.

The diagram shows an example of a situation where three forces sum to zero; it illustrates a vehicle parked on a hill at rest and a vector triangle that shows the forces.

> A normal reaction force acts on all four wheels; the arrow shown on the diagram represents the sum of these forces.

> When net force is zero, as here, then Newton's first law tells us that the motion must be unchanging and that the body cannot be accelerating.

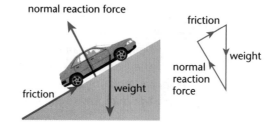

The third law

AQA B   4
OCR A   G484

This is both the simplest in its statement and the most misunderstood of the three laws. The statement given here is not a direct translation of the original, but it helps to remove some of the misunderstanding.

> The laws were originally written in Latin. The third law is directly translated as 'to every action there is an equal and opposite reaction'. This was widely misinterpreted as meaning that two equal and opposite forces act on the same object, resulting in zero acceleration.

> **KEY POINT**
>
> Newton's third law can be stated as:
>
> If object A exerts a force on object B, then B exerts a force of the same type, equal in size and opposite in direction on A.

According to the third law, forces do not exist individually but in pairs. However, it is important to remember that:

- the forces are of the same type, i.e. both gravitational or electrical
- the forces act on different objects
- the third law applies to all situations.

Some examples

AQA B   4
OCR A   G484

Application of Newton's third law can lead to some surprising results. If you step off a wall the Earth pulls you down towards the ground. According to the third law, you also pull the Earth up with an equal-sized force. So why doesn't the Earth accelerate upwards to meet you instead of the other way round? The answer is it does, but if you apply $F = ma$ to work out the Earth's acceleration, it turns out to be minimal.

Newton's third law: pairs of forces that are equal in size and opposite in direction

Key point from AS

• force =
  mass × acceleration
  Revise AS section 1.6

This type of situation is where the greatest misunderstanding of Newton's third law occurs. Remember, third law pairs of forces act on **different** objects.

Planets pull moons and, according to the third law, moons pull planets with an equal-sized force. Why does the moon go round the planet instead of the other way round?

Again, the answer is it does. In fact, they both rotate around a common centre of mass. In the case of the Earth and its Moon, the centre of mass is relatively close to the centre of the Earth so it is a reasonable approximation to say that the Moon orbits the Earth.

The diagram shows another pair of forces that are equal in size and opposite in direction. This is an application of the **first** law – the vase is in a state of rest so there is no resultant force acting on it.

the Earth pulls the vase

the table pushes the vase

These forces are equal in size and opposite in direction acting on a single object – an application of Newton's first law, not third.

Forces acting on bodies in lifts

AQA B   4
OCR A   G484

When a body is accelerating, there *must* be a net (unbalanced) force acting on it. When it is not accelerating (whether stationary or with a constant velocity that is not zero), then the net force *must* be zero.

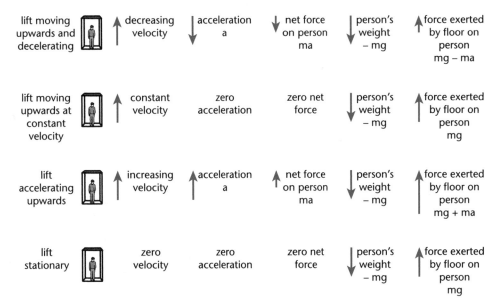

Note the close link between force and acceleration – always in the same direction, and when one is zero then so is the other.

lift moving upwards and decelerating	↑ decreasing velocity	↓ acceleration a	↓ net force on person ma	↓ person's weight – mg	↑ force exerted by floor on person mg – ma
lift moving upwards at constant velocity	↑ constant velocity	zero acceleration	zero net force	↓ person's weight – mg	↑ force exerted by floor on person mg
lift accelerating upwards	↑ increasing velocity	↑ acceleration a	↑ net force on person ma	↓ person's weight – mg	↑ force exerted by floor on person mg + ma
lift stationary	zero velocity	zero acceleration	zero net force	↓ person's weight – mg	↑ force exerted by floor on person mg

Note that the net force acting on the person is the resultant of their weight and the upwards force that the floor exerts on them.

Progress check

1 Explain why a driving force is needed to maintain motion on the surface of the Earth.

2 Suggest why the driving force needed to maintain motion on the surface of the Moon is less than for the same vehicle on the surface of the Earth.

3 A foot kicks a ball. What are the forces that make up the pair in the sense of the third law?

3 The ball pushes the foot.
2 There is no air resistance on the Moon.
1 The driving force is needed to balance the resistive forces that oppose motion.

1.2 Momentum and the second law

After studying this section you should be able to

- apply the principle of conservation of momentum to collisions in one dimension
- state the relationship between the change of momentum of an object and the resultant force on it
- explain the difference between an elastic and an inelastic collision

LEARNING SUMMARY

Momentum

AQA A	4	Edexcel context	4
AQA B	4	OCR A	G484
CCEA	A2.1	OCR B	G494
Edexcel concept	4	WJEC	4

> A collision between two objects need not involve physical contact. Imagine two positive charges approaching each other; the repulsive forces could cause them to reverse in direction without actually touching.

Which is more effective at demolishing a brick wall, a 1 kg iron ball moving at 50 m s⁻¹ or a 1000 kg iron ball moving at 1 m s⁻¹? Both the mass and the velocity need to be taken into account to answer this question.

No matter how hard you throw a tennis ball at a garden wall you will not knock the wall down; nor will you be very successful if you use a tennis ball to play ten-pin bowling!

Newton realised that what happens to a moving object involved in a collision depends on two factors:

- the mass of the object
- the velocity of the object.

He used the concept of **momentum** to explain the results of collisions between objects.

> A ten-pin bowling ball has a mass of several kilogrammes, so even at low speeds it has much more momentum than a tennis ball (mass 0.06 kg) travelling as fast as you can throw it.

> **KEY POINT**
>
> momentum = mass × velocity
>
> $p = m \times v$
>
> Momentum is a vector quantity, the direction being the same as that of the velocity. It is measured in N s or kg m s⁻¹; these units are equivalent.

Everything that moves has momentum and can exert a force on anything that it interacts with. This applies as much to the light that is hitting you at the moment as it does to a collision between two vehicles.

Conservation of momentum

AQA A	4	Edexcel context	4
AQA B	4	OCR A	G484
CCEA	A2.1	OCR B	G494
Edexcel concept	4	WJEC	4

> The phrase 'equal and opposite' is used as a shorthand way of writing 'equal in size and opposite in direction'.

When a force causes an object to change its velocity, there is also a change in its momentum. When two objects interact or collide, they exert equal and opposite forces on each other and so the momentum of each one changes. This is illustrated in the diagram, where the blue ball loses momentum and the black ball gains momentum.

before		after	
5.0 m s⁻¹	3.0 m s⁻¹	4.2 m s⁻¹	6.2 m s⁻¹
0.4 kg	0.1 kg	0.4 kg	0.1 kg

Like the forces they exert on each other during the collision, the changes in momentum of the balls are *equal in size and opposite in direction*.

It follows that:

- the combined momentum of the balls is the same before and after they collide.

Since p = mv and kinetic energy is given by

$E_k = \frac{1}{2}mv^2$,

the two quantities are related by the formula

$E_k = \frac{p^2}{2m}$

This is an example of the **principle of conservation of momentum**.

> **KEY POINT**
>
> The principle of conservation of momentum states that:
>
> When two or more objects interact the total momentum remains constant provided that there is no external resultant force.

In the context of the colliding balls, an external resultant force could be due to friction or something hitting one of the balls. Either of these would result in a change in the total momentum.

Different types of interaction

AQA A	4	Edexcel context	4
AQA B	4	OCR A	G484
CCEA	A2.1	OCR B	G494
Edexcel concept	4	WJEC	4

Objects moving in opposite directions

When two objects approach each other and 'collide' head-on, the result of the collision depends on whether they stick together or whether one or both rebound.

The diagram shows two 'vehicles' approaching each other on an air track. The vehicles join together and move as one.

To make two air track vehicles stick together, one has some Plasticine stuck to it and the other is fitted with a pin that sticks into the Plasticine.

0.40 m s⁻¹	0.30 m s⁻¹	velocity = ?
0.30 kg	0.20 kg	0.50 kg
before		after

The principle of conservation of momentum can be used to work out the combined velocity, v, after the collision.

Taking velocity from left to right as being positive:

total momentum before collision =
$$0.3 \text{ kg} \times + 0.4 \text{ m s}^{-1} + 0.2 \text{ kg} \times - 0.3 \text{ m s}^{-1} = 0.06 \text{ N s}.$$

This must equal the momentum after the collision, so $0.5 \text{ kg} \times v = 0.06 \text{ N s}$,

i.e. $v = 0.12 \text{ m s}^{-1}$. As this is positive, it follows that the 'vehicle' is moving from left to right.

Rebound

When a light object collides with a heavier one, the light object may rebound, reversing the direction of its momentum. The diagram shows an example of such a collision.

A rebound collision can be modelled on an air track by fitting the vehicles with repelling magnets.

before		after	
10 m s⁻¹	0 m s⁻¹	v	3.33 m s⁻¹
2 kg	10 kg		

The figures here are rounded. The 3.3 is a rounded value of 3⅓.

Application of the principle of conservation of momentum in this case gives:

$$2 \text{ kg} \times 10 \text{ m s}^{-1} + 10 \text{ kg} \times 0 \text{ m s}^{-1} = 2 \text{ kg} \times v + 10 \text{ kg} \times 3.3 \text{ m s}^{-1}$$

So $v = -6.7 \text{ m s}^{-1}$. The significance of the negative sign is that the green ball is now travelling from right to left.

Recoil

In some situations two objects are stationary before they interact, having a combined momentum of zero. After they interact, both objects move off but the combined momentum is still zero. Examples of this include:

- a stationary nucleus undergoes radioactive decay, giving off an alpha particle
- a person steps off a boat onto the quayside
- two ice skaters stand facing each other; then one pushes the other
- two air track 'vehicles' fitted with repelling magnets are held together and then released.

In each case, both objects start moving from rest. For the combined momentum to remain zero, each object must gain the same amount of momentum but these momentum gains must be in *opposite directions*. Such an interaction is sometimes called an explosion.

The ice skater who does the pushing **recoils** as an equal and opposite force is exerted by the one who is pushed.

In the example shown in the diagram above, an 80 kg man pushes a 50 kg child. Their combined momentum is zero both before and after this interaction.

Taking velocity from left to right as positive, this means that:

$$80 \text{ kg} \times -0.6 \text{ m s}^{-1} + 50 \text{ kg} \times v = 0$$

So v, the velocity of the child after the interaction, is 0.96 m s^{-1} to the right.

Elastic or inelastic

AQA A	4	Edexcel context	4
AQA B	4	OCR A	G484
CCEA	A2.1	OCR B	G494
Edexcel concept	4	WJEC	4

In all three examples above, both momentum and energy are conserved. This is always the case. A collision where the total **kinetic** energy before and after the interaction is the same is called an **elastic** collision. Where there is a gain or loss of kinetic energy as a result of the interaction the collision is called **inelastic**.

In an elastic collision: momentum, kinetic energy and total energy are conserved.

In an inelastic collision: momentum and total energy are conserved, but the amount of kinetic energy changes.

Momentum and the second law

AQA A	4	OCR A	G484
AQA B	4	OCR B	G494
CCEA	A2.1	WJEC	4
Edexcel context	4		

Newton's second law establishes the relationship between the resultant force acting on an object and the change of momentum that it causes. An important result that follows from the second law and the definition of the newton is F = m × a.

> **Newton's second law states that:**
>
> The rate of change of momentum of an object is proportional to the resultant force acting on it and acts in the direction of the resultant force.
>
> $$\Delta p/\Delta t \propto F$$

KEY POINT

Key points from AS

- **The definition of the size of the newton.**
  Revise AS section 1.6

The definition of the size of the newton fixes the proportionality constant at one. This enables the second law to be written as:

> **Force = rate of change of momentum**
> $F = \Delta p/\Delta t$

KEY POINT

In this form, the second law is useful for working out the force in situations such as jet and rocket propulsion where the change in momentum each second can be calculated easily.

Jet and rocket engines use the same principle; hot gases are ejected from the back of the engine to provide a force in the forwards direction. The difference is that jet engines are designed to operate within the Earth's atmosphere, so they can take oxygen from their surroundings.

A rocket carries its own oxygen supply, so that it can fire the engines when it is travelling in a vacuum. A spacecraft travelling where it is not affected by any gravitational fields or resistive forces maintains a constant velocity, so it only needs to fire the rocket engines to change speed or direction.

The principle of rocket propulsion can be seen by blowing up a balloon and letting it go; the air squashed out of the neck of the balloon gains momentum as it leaves, causing the balloon and the air that remains inside to gain momentum at the same rate but in the opposite direction. The diagram shows the principle of rocket propulsion.

The unit kg m s^{-2} is equivalent to the N, so a rate of change of momentum of 4 500 000 kg m s^{-2} is another way of stating: a force of 4 500 000 N.

exhaust gases gain momentum in this direction

rocket gains momentum in this direction

conservation of momentum and rocket propulsion

The equation $F = \dfrac{\Delta p}{\Delta t}$ is the same as the equation $F = ma$. The latter equation shows that for a body of fixed mass, the force and acceleration vary in fixed proportion.

In this example, the exhaust gases are emitted at a rate of 3000 kg s^{-1}. The speed of the exhaust gases relative to the rocket is 1500 m s^{-1}. The rate of change of momentum of these gases is therefore 4 500 000 kg m s^{-2}, i.e. 4 500 000 kg m s^{-1} each second. The size of the force on both the gases and the rocket is 4 500 000 N.

Progress check

1. Two vehicles fitted with repelling magnets are held together on an air track. The masses of the vehicles are 0.10 kg and 0.15 kg.

   The vehicles are released. The 0.10 kg vehicle moves to the left with a speed of 0.24 m s^{-1}. Calculate the velocity of the heavier vehicle.

2. A ball of mass 0.020 kg hits a wall at a speed of 12.5 m s^{-1} and rebounds at a speed of 10.0 m s^{-1}.
   a. Calculate the change in momentum of the ball.
   b. If the ball is in contact with the wall for 0.010 s, calculate the size of the force between the ball and the wall.
   c. Explain whether this collision is elastic or inelastic.

c Inelastic. The ball has less kinetic energy after rebound than before it hits the wall.
b 45 N
2 a 0.45 N s in the direction of the rebound
1 0.16 m s^{-1} to the right

1.3 Motion in a circle

After studying this section you should be able to:

- use the radian to measure angular displacement
- describe the forces on an object moving in a circle
- recall and use the expressions for centripetal force and centripetal acceleration

LEARNING SUMMARY

Measuring angles

AQA A	4	Edexcel context	4
AQA B	4	OCR A	C484
CCEA	A2.1	OCR B	C494
Edexcel concept	4	WJEC	4

When an object travels through a complete circle it moves through an angle of 360°, although the distance it travels depends on the radius of the circle. When a train or motor vehicle travels round a bend, the outer wheels have further to travel than the inner wheels. Similarly, when a compact disc is being played all points on the disc move through the same angle in any given time, but the linear speed at any point depends on its distance from the centre.

An alternative unit to the degree for measuring angular displacement is the radian, defined as the arc length divided by the radius of the circle. This is shown in the diagram.

> Angle θ is 1 radian when $x = r$.

$$\theta = \frac{x}{r}$$

Measuring an angle in radians

> To convert an angle in degrees to one in radians, multiply by π and divide by 180.

It follows that movement through one complete circle, or 360°, is equal to a displacement of θ = circumference ÷ radius = $2\pi r \div r = 2\pi$ radians.

Speed in a circle

AQA A	4	Edexcel context	4
AQA B	4	OCR A	C484
CCEA	A2.1	OCR B	C494
Edexcel concept	4	WJEC	4

When an object moves in a circular path its velocity is always at right angles to a radial line, a line joining it to the centre of the circle.

Two objects, such as points on a CD, at different distances from the centre each complete the same number of revolutions in any specified time but they have different speeds. They have the same angular velocity but different linear velocities.

> Angular velocity is a vector quantity that can have one of two directions: clockwise or anticlockwise.

> **Angular velocity, ω, is defined as:**
> *the rate of change of angular displacement with time.*
> It is represented by the gradient of an angular displacement–time graph.
> average angular velocity = angular displacement ÷ time
> $$\omega = \Delta\theta/\Delta t$$
> where $\Delta\theta$ is the angular displacement in time Δt.
>
> KEY POINT

The relationship between angular velocity and linear velocity for an object moving in a circle of radius r is:

$$v = r\omega.$$

The **time period** for one revolution, T, is equal to the angular displacement (2π radians) divided by the angular velocity:

$$T = 2\pi/\omega.$$

The frequency of a circular motion, f, is equal to 1/T:

$$f = 1/T = \omega/2\pi.$$

$\omega = 2\pi f$

Some specifications use ω while others always write $2\pi f$.

Centripetal acceleration

AQA A	4	Edexcel context	4
AQA B	4	OCR A	G484
CCEA	A2.1	OCR B	G494
Edexcel concept	4	WJEC	4

Any object that changes its velocity is accelerating. Since velocity involves both speed and direction, a change in either of these quantities is an acceleration. An object moving at a constant speed in a circle is therefore accelerating as it is continually changing its direction. The vector diagram below shows the change in velocity, Δv, for an object following a circular path. This change in direction is always towards the centre of the circle.

Note that Δv is the change in velocity from v_1 to v_2, so
$v_1 + \Delta v = v_2$

The change in direction of an object following a circular path

The acceleration of an object moving in a circle:

- is called **centripetal acceleration**
- is directed towards the centre of the circle.

Centripetal acceleration, a, is the acceleration of an object moving in a circular path.

$$a = v^2/r = r\omega^2$$

where v is the linear velocity, ω is the angular velocity and r is the radius of the circle.

The unbalanced force

AQA A	4	Edexcel context	4
AQA B	4	OCR A	G484
CCEA	A2.1	OCR B	G494
Edexcel concept	4	WJEC	4

To make an object accelerate, there has to be an unbalanced force acting in the same direction as the acceleration (see Newton's first law). In the case of circular motion the unbalanced force is called the **centripetal force**.

It is important to understand that the centripetal force is the resultant of all the forces acting on an object. A common misconception is that it is an extra force that appears when an object moves in a circular path.

When a train travels around a bend, the centripetal force comes from the push of the outer rail on the wheel. For a road vehicle such as a car, bus or bicycle it is the push of the road on the tyres; if there is insufficient friction due to ice or a slippery surface, the vehicle does not complete the turn and may leave the road.

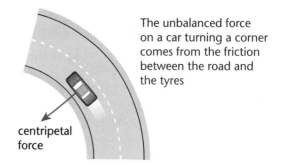

The unbalanced force on a car turning a corner comes from the friction between the road and the tyres

centripetal force

The size of the unbalanced force required to maintain circular motion can be calculated using F = ma:

> An object moving at constant speed in a circular path requires an unbalanced force towards the centre of the circle.
>
> centripetal force, $F = mv^2/r = mr\omega^2$

The theme park ride

AQA A	4	Edexcel context	4
AQA B	4	OCR A	G484
CCEA	A2.1	OCR B	G494
Edexcel concept	4	WJEC	4

You feel the apparent change in weight when you travel in a lift. As the lift accelerates upwards you feel heavier because the normal contact force is greater than your weight.

Key points from AS

• **Vector diagrams**
  Revise AS section 1.1

Check that in each case the resultant of the forces is equal to mv^2/r towards the centre of the circle.

Some theme park rides involve motion in a vertical circle. Part of the thrill of being on one of these rides is the apparent change in weight as you travel round the circle. This is because the force that you feel as you sit or stand is not your weight, but the normal contact force pushing up. If the forces on you are balanced, this force is equal in size to your weight, but it can become bigger or smaller if the forces are unbalanced, causing you to feel heavier or lighter.

The diagram below shows the forces acting on a person moving in a vertical circle when they are at the top and bottom of the circle.

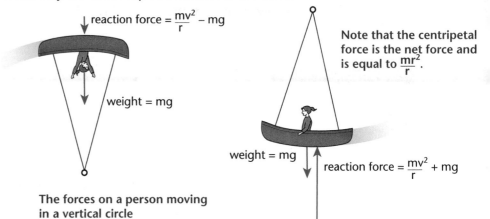

reaction force $= \dfrac{mv^2}{r} - mg$

weight = mg

Note that the centripetal force is the net force and is equal to $\dfrac{mr^2}{r}$.

weight = mg

reaction force $= \dfrac{mv^2}{r} + mg$

The forces on a person moving in a vertical circle

At the bottom of the circle:
• The person feels heavier than usual as the size of the normal reaction force is equal to the person's weight plus the centripetal force required to maintain circular motion.

At the top of the circle:

Another possibility is that the speed of the ride is such that the required centripetal force is less than the person's weight. In this case a safety harness is required to stop the person from falling out.

• The person may feel lighter than usual as the person's weight is providing part of the centripetal force required to maintain circular motion. The rest comes from the normal reaction force, which is less than the person's weight if $mv^2/r < 2mg$.

• If the speed of the ride is such that the required centripetal force is the same as the person's weight then he or she feels 'weightless' as the normal reaction force is zero.

Moment of inertia

AQA A	5
AQA B	4

Moment of inertia is a measure of the resistance of a body to rotational acceleration. As such, it is comparable to mass of a body as a measure of resistance to linear acceleration.

$$\text{Note that mass, } m = \frac{\text{force}}{\text{linear acceleration}}$$

$$\text{and moment of inertia, } I = \frac{\text{torque}}{\text{angular acceleration}}$$

where torque = force × perpendicular distance from force to axis of rotation

$$\text{angular acceleration} = \frac{\Delta\omega}{\Delta t}$$

Moment of inertia depends on the mass of a body and its distance from the axis of rotation.

$I = mr^2$ Note that the unit of moment of inertia is kg m²

For a mass m in circular motion, r is simply the radius of orbit.

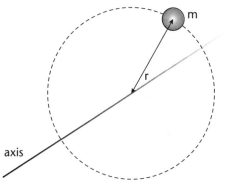

For a symmetrical cylinder rotating about a central axis, $I = \frac{1}{2}mr^2$

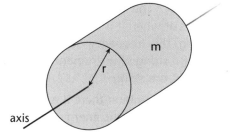

All rotating bodies conserve angular momentum just as bodies in linear motion conserve linear momentum.

Angular momentum = $I\omega$

Rotating bodies possess angular kinetic energy:

Angular kinetic energy = $\frac{1}{2}I\omega^2$

THE HENLEY COLLEGE LIBRARY

Progress check

1 a   Convert into radians:
   i   90°
   ii 720°
  b   An object is displaced through an angle of 8π radians.
      Explain why it has returned to its original position.

2 A stone is tied to a string and whirled round in a horizontal circle.
  a   What is providing the centripetal force?
  b   The stone moves at a horizontal speed of 3.5 m s⁻¹.
      The radius of the circle is 2.0 m.
      Calculate the centripetal acceleration.
  c   Calculate the size of the centripetal force if the mass of the stone is 0.25 kg.

1.4 Oscillations, resonance and damping

After studying this section you should be able to:

- *explain the difference between a free and a forced vibration*
- *describe resonance and how it occurs*
- *distinguish between a damped oscillation and an undamped one and give examples of each*

LEARNING SUMMARY

Oscillations

AQA A	4	Edexcel context	5
AQA B	4	OCR A	G484
CCEA	A2.1	OCR B	G494
Edexcel concept	5	WJEC	4

The terms 'oscillation' and 'vibration' have the same meaning. They are both used to describe a regular to-and-fro movement.

An **oscillation** is a repetitive to-and-fro movement. Loudspeaker cones oscillate, as do swings in a children's playground. However, there is an important difference between these oscillations.

The loudspeaker cone is an example of a **forced vibration**; the cone is forced to vibrate at the frequency of the current that passes in the coil. The amplitude of vibration depends on the size of the current. When reproducing speech or music, the frequency of vibration is constantly changing.

A child's swing, like a string on a piano or a guitar is an example of a **free vibration**. Once displaced from its normal position, it vibrates at its own **natural frequency**. The natural frequency of vibration of an object is the frequency it vibrates at when it is displaced from its normal, or rest, position and released. For a swing, this frequency depends only on the length of the chain or rope; in the case of a stringed instrument it is also affected by the tension and mass per unit length of the string.

The vibration of particles in a solid is a free vibration. Like a swing, the energy of the particles changes from kinetic to potential (stored) energy.

- In a free vibration there is a constant interchange between potential (stored) energy and kinetic energy.
- A swing has zero kinetic energy and maximum gravitational potential energy when at its greatest displacement; the kinetic energy is at a maximum and the gravitational potential energy at a minimum when the displacement is zero. This is shown in the diagram.

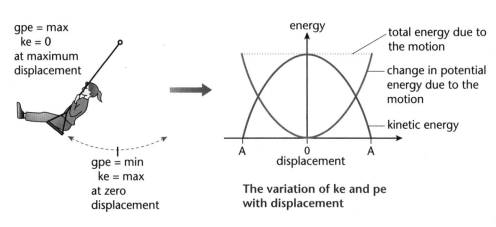

gpe = max
ke = 0
at maximum
displacement

gpe = min
ke = max
at zero
displacement

energy

total energy due to the motion

change in potential energy due to the motion

kinetic energy

A   0   A
displacement

The variation of ke and pe with displacement

total energy = $E_k + E_p$

Resonance

AQA A	4	Edexcel context	5
AQA B	4	OCR A	G484
CCEA	A2.1	OCR B	G494
Edexcel concept	5	WJEC	4

There are many everyday examples of resonance. You may have noticed windows vibrating due to the sound from a bus waiting at a stop. Electrical resonance is used to tune in a radio or television to a particular station.

After a swing is given a push, it vibrates at its natural frequency. To make it swing higher, subsequent pushes need to coincide with the vibrations of the swing. This is an example of **resonance**, the large amplitude oscillation that occurs when the frequency of a forced vibration is equal to the natural frequency of the vibrating object.

The diagram shows how a vibration generator can be used to force a string to vibrate at any frequency, and the large amplitude vibration that occurs when the driving frequency coincides with the natural frequency of the string, also called its **resonant frequency**. At this frequency the string is able to absorb sufficient energy from the vibration generator to replace the energy lost due to resistive forces.

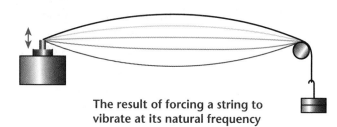

The result of forcing a string to vibrate at its natural frequency

If the frequency of the forced oscillation is increased slowly from zero, the amplitude of vibration of the string starts to increase at a frequency below the resonant frequency. It has its maximum value at this frequency and it then decreases again as the frequency continues to increase. The variation of amplitude around the resonant frequency is shown below.

The sharpness of the peak depends on the resistive forces acting. The greater the resistive force, the smaller the amplitude of vibration.

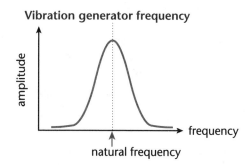

Vibration generator frequency

amplitude — frequency

natural frequency

These are some practical examples of resonance.

- Microwave cookers heat food by causing water molecules in the food to resonate, absorbing the energy from the microwaves.

- Magnetic resonance imaging (MRI) is used in medicine to produce a detailed picture of the inside of the body by making the atomic nuclei resonate.

- Resonance in mechanical systems can be a nuisance or a danger. When the frequency of the engine vibrations in a vehicle matches the natural frequency of the exhaust system the result is a rattle as the exhaust system vibrates against the body of the vehicle.

- Resonance of parts of aircraft can cause failure due to excessive stress and several helicopter crashes have been attributed to resonance of the pilot's eyeballs resulting in the pilot being unable to see overhead power lines.

Damping

AQA A	4	Edexcel context	5
AQA B	4	OCR A	G484
CCEA	A2.1	OCR B	G494
Edexcel concept	5	WJEC	4

Just as for linear motion, all mechanical oscillations are subject to resistive forces. The effect of resistive forces in removing energy from a vibrating object is known as **damping**.

A string or mass on a spring vibrating in air is **lightly damped** as the main resistive force is air resistance. The effect of light damping is to gradually reduce the energy, and therefore amplitude, of the vibrating object.

> A car mechanic tests the shock absorbers by pushing down on the car bonnet. If the car oscillates, the shock absorbers need replacing.

The body of a motor vehicle is connected to the wheels by springs. When the vehicle goes over a bump in the road the springs compress, giving the passengers a smoother ride. If motor vehicles were lightly damped they would continue to oscillate after going over a bump. Shock absorbers increase the resistive force, so that when the body of the vehicle has been displaced it returns to its original position without oscillating. A motor vehicle is **critically damped** so that it returns to the normal position in the minimum time to avoid vibrations that could cause 'car-sickness' and possibly loss of control by the driver.

Very large resistive forces result in **heavy damping**. Imagine a mass on a spring suspended so that the mass is in a viscous liquid such as syrup. If the mass is displaced, the force opposing its movement is very large and it takes a long time to return to the normal position.

> The effect of damping is to transfer the energy from the vibrating object to heat the surroundings.

One effect of damping is to decrease the effects of resonance. The greater the damping, the smaller the amplitude of vibration at the resonant frequency. This is very important in mechanical structures such as bridges which can resonate due to the effects of wind. Resonance caused the suspension bridge built over the Tacoma Narrows, in America, to collapse in 1939. Since then, engineers have designed suspension bridges with shock absorbers built into the suspension to absorb the energy and prevent excessive vibration.

Progress check

1 Describe the difference between a free vibration and a forced vibration.
2 Explain why a washing machine sometimes vibrates violently when the drum is spinning.
3 Explain how a free vibration is affected by the amount of damping.

3 Damping removes energy from a vibrating object. Increasing the damping reduces the amplitude of vibration and may stop any vibration from occurring.
2 The washing machine has a natural frequency of vibration. If the drum rotates at this frequency it causes the machine to resonate.
1 A free vibration occurs when an object is displaced and it vibrates at its natural frequency. A forced vibration can be at any frequency and is caused by an external oscillating force.

1.5 Simple harmonic motion

After studying this section you should be able to:

- *explain what is meant by simple harmonic motion*
- *apply the equations of simple harmonic motion*
- *sketch graphs showing the change in displacement, velocity and acceleration in simple harmonic motion*

LEARNING SUMMARY

What is simple harmonic motion?

AQA A	4	Edexcel context	5
AQA B	4	OCR A	G484
CCEA	A2.1	OCR B	G494
Edexcel concept	5	WJEC	4

The resultant force on an object in simple harmonic motion is a restoring force since it is always directed towards the equilibrium position that the object has been displaced from.

As the name implies, it is the simplest kind of oscillatory motion. One set of equations can be used to describe and predict the movement of any object whose motion is simple harmonic.

The motion of a vibrating object is simple harmonic if:

- its acceleration is proportional to its displacement
- its acceleration and displacement are in opposite directions.

The second bullet point means that the acceleration, and therefore the resultant force, always acts towards the equilibrium position, where the displacement is zero.

Common examples of simple harmonic motion (often abbreviated to shm) include the oscillations of a simple pendulum (provided the amplitude is small, equivalent to an angular displacement of less than about 10°) and those of a mass suspended vertically on a spring.

The diagram shows how accelerations are related to displacements, x, from equilibrium positions.

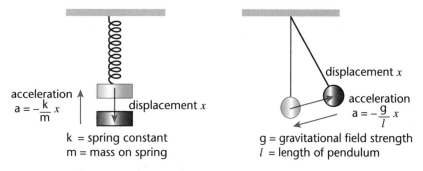

acceleration $a = -\dfrac{k}{m}x$ displacement x

k = spring constant
m = mass on spring

displacement x

acceleration $a = -\dfrac{g}{l}x$

g = gravitational field strength
l = length of pendulum

k, the spring constant, is defined as the force per unit extension
$k = F/x$

- the numerical value of the acceleration is equal to a constant multiplied by the displacement, showing that acceleration is proportional to displacement
- the negative value of the acceleration shows that it is in the opposite direction to the displacement.

Frequency of simple harmonic motion

AQA A	4	Edexcel context	5
AQA B	4	OCR A	G484
CCEA	A2.1	OCR B	G494
Edexcel concept	5	WJEC	4

Since $(2\pi f)^2$ is always positive, a and x have the opposite signs so they are always in opposite directions.

> The acceleration of any object whose motion is simple harmonic is related to the frequency of vibration by the equation:
>
> $$a = -(2\pi f)^2 x$$
>
> where a is the acceleration, f is the frequency and x is the displacement.

KEY POINT

Simple harmonic motion is like circular motion in that it repeats over and over again – it is cyclic. The mathematics of circular motion is therefore useful for describing and predicting simple harmonic motion. As for circular motion, the 'angular velocity' of simple harmonic motion is written as ω (omega), and is equal to $2\pi f$. Some specifications use $2\pi f$ in equations, while others use ω so that the above equation becomes:

$$a = -\omega^2 x$$

The remainder of this section uses $2\pi f$.

Key points from AS

• **The difference between distance and displacement**
Revise AS section 1.5

A graph of acceleration against displacement is therefore a straight line through the origin, as shown in the diagram. The gradient of the graph has a negative value and is numerically equal to $(2\pi f)^2$.

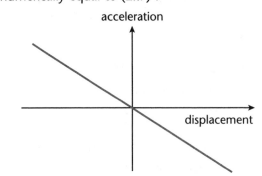

The constants in the equations for the acceleration of the mass on a spring (constant = k/m) and the pendulum bob (constant = g/l) give useful information about the frequency and time period of the oscillation.

For a mass on a spring:

$$(2\pi f)^2 = k/m$$

The relationship between the frequency, f, and the time period, T, is $f = 1/T$ so each of these quantities is the reciprocal of the other.

So:

> **KEY POINT**
> $$f = \frac{1}{2\pi}\sqrt{\frac{k}{m}} \quad \text{and} \quad T = 2\pi\sqrt{\frac{m}{k}}$$

For a simple pendulum:

$$(2\pi f)^2 = g/l$$

So:

> **KEY POINT**
> $$f = \frac{1}{2\pi}\sqrt{\frac{g}{l}} \quad \text{and} \quad T = 2\pi\sqrt{\frac{l}{g}}$$

These equations for frequency and time period show that:

The spring constant, k, is a measure of the stiffness of a spring.

• increasing the mass on a spring causes the frequency to decrease and the time period to increase
• for a given mass, the stiffer the spring the higher the frequency of oscillation
• the frequency and time period of a pendulum do not depend on the mass of the pendulum bob, as m does not appear in the equation
• increasing the length of a pendulum causes the frequency to decrease and the time period to increase.

Displacement and time

AQA A	4	Edexcel context	5
AQA B	4	OCR A	G484
CCEA	A2.1	OCR B	G494
Edexcel concept	5	WJEC	4

The displacement of an object in simple harmonic motion varies sinusoidally with time. This means that a displacement–time graph has the shape of a sine or cosine curve, and the displacement at any time, t, can be written in terms of a sine or cosine function.

The symbol x_0 is also used as an alternative to A to represent amplitude.

> **KEY POINT**
>
> The displacement of an object in simple harmonic motion can be calculated using either of the equations:
>
> $$x = A \sin 2\pi ft$$
> $$x = A \cos 2\pi ft$$
>
> where A is the amplitude of the motion.

The graphs below show the variation of displacement with time for a simple harmonic motion.

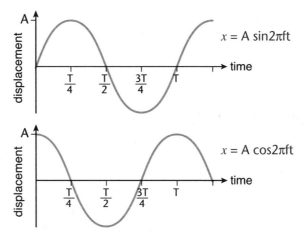

Which equation and graph apply to a simple harmonic motion depends on the displacement when the time is zero.

Sine and cosine are identical functions with a 90°, or $\pi/2$ radians, phase difference.

- If the displacement is zero at time t = 0, then the sine applies.
- If the displacement is at the maximum at time t = 0, then the cosine applies.

Displacement, velocity and acceleration

AQA A	4	Edexcel context	5
AQA B	4	OCR A	G484
CCEA	A2.1	OCR B	G494
Edexcel concept	5	WJEC	4

These bullet points apply to any motion.

Displacement, velocity and acceleration are linked graphically because:

- the gradient of a displacement–time graph represents velocity
- the gradient of a velocity–time graph represents acceleration.

The following diagram shows the variation of all three variables for a simple harmonic motion where the variation of the displacement with time is represented by a sine function.

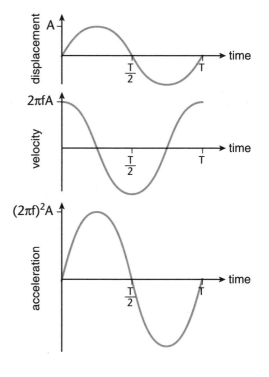

These graphs show that:

- when the displacement is zero the velocity is at a maximum and the acceleration is zero
- when the displacement has its maximum value the velocity is zero and the acceleration is a maximum in the opposite direction.

Knowledge of the frequency and amplitude of a simple harmonic motion enables the maximum speed and the velocity at any displacement to be calculated.

> These statements about the acceleration follow from the definition of simple harmonic motion.

> The ± symbol is used because at any value of the displacement the velocity could be in either direction.

> **KEY POINT**
>
> The maximum speed of an object in simple harmonic motion is:
> $$v = \pm 2\pi fA$$
> The relationship between velocity and displacement is:
> $$v = \pm 2\pi f \sqrt{(A^2 - x^2)}$$

Progress check

When a 100 g mass is attached to the bottom of a vertical spring it causes it to extend by 5.0 cm.

a Calculate the value of the spring constant, k.
Assume $g = 10$ N kg^{-1}.
The mass is pulled down a further 3 cm and released.

b Calculate the frequency and time period of the resulting oscillation.

c i What is the value of the amplitude of the oscillation?
ii Calculate the maximum speed of the mass.

a 20 N m^{-1}
b 2.25 Hz and 0.44 s
c i 3 cm
ii 0.42 m s^{-1}

1.6 Relativity

After studying this section you should be able to:

- recall the postulates of special relativity
- calculate the amount of time dilation and length contraction when a moving object is observed
- explain why there is a maximum speed to which an object can be accelerated

LEARNING SUMMARY

Does time pass at a constant rate?

AQA A	5	OCR B	G494
AQA B	5	WJEC	5
Edexcel concept	4		
Edexcel context	4		

In everyday life, we sense and judge speed relative to the surface of the Earth or vehicles that we travel in. If you are in a car travelling at 25 m s⁻¹ and another car travelling at the same speed is approaching you, then its speed relative to your vehicle is 50 m s⁻¹. If, on the other hand, it is in front of you and travelling in the same direction, its speed relative to you is zero.

Each car has its own **frame of reference** and a pedestrian on the roadside has a different frame of reference again. Measurements of the same motion from different frames of reference can produce different answers. **Special relativity** considers only frames of reference that are not accelerating.

> The laws of physics apply equally in all non-accelerating frames of reference.
>
> This is the first postulate (assumption) of Einstein's theory of special relativity.

KEY POINT

In the diagram, the driver of the red car sees the blue car approaching at 50 m s⁻¹ but, from the frame of reference of the stationary observer, the blue car is approaching at 30 m s⁻¹.

20 m/s   30 m/s

What about the light that passes between the two vehicles? Are the different measurements of its speed by the drivers and pedestrian affected by their motion? For anything else the answer would be 'yes', but for light the answer is 'no'.

Light is special – it does not behave like objects such as cars. Measurements of its speed in air or in a vacuum all give the same answer, whether or not there is relative motion of the observer and the source of light.

> The speed of light in a vacuum always has the same value in any frame of reference, whether or not the light originated in another frame of reference.
>
> This is the second postulate of Einstein's theory.

KEY POINT

The invariance in the speed of light leads to the conclusion that neither time nor distance have absolute values. For most people this is a surprising conclusion – the idea that there is no single universal time but that measurement of time in other frames of reference can vary when there is relative motion is an idea that takes

Far more muons reach the surface of the Earth than is predicted by a half-life of 2 microseconds. But the apparent half-life of muons created in the upper atmosphere increases from 2 microseconds to 20 microseconds, measured by an observer on Earth. The muons move through the atmosphere at a speed which is within 1% of that of light.

some getting used to. Each of the drivers of the cars in the diagram would notice that time passes ever so slightly more slowly in the other vehicle. This effect is known as **time dilation**, and it is an effect that increases as relative speed increases. We do not normally notice the effects of time dilation because we move at speeds very much less than the speed of light.

As well as having different measurements of time, the car drivers in the diagram have different measurements of distance. Each driver sees the other car as being shorter than its driver sees it; this is known as **length contraction**. Length contraction only occurs in the direction of motion.

> **KEY POINT**
>
> The factor by which time is dilated and length is contracted is $\sqrt{1 - \dfrac{v^2}{c^2}}$,
>
> where v is the speed of the object relative to the observer and c is the speed of light.

It follows that time t_0 and length l_0 measured within a frame of reference are observed by someone moving relative to that frame to have values:

- $t = t_0 / \sqrt{(1 - v^2/c^2)}$
- $l = l_0 \sqrt{(1 - v^2/c^2)}$

How is mass affected?

AQA A	5	Edexcel context	4
AQA B	5	OCR B	G494
Edexcel concept	4	WJEC	5

A consequence of length contraction is that as an object speeds up under the action of a constant force, its apparent acceleration decreases. This is matched by an apparent increase in mass.

For everyday objects moving at everyday speeds, there is no significant increase in mass.

> **KEY POINT**
>
> The apparent mass, m, is given by the expression
>
> $$m = \frac{m_0}{\sqrt{(1 - v^2/c^2)}}$$
>
> where m_0 is the **rest mass**, the mass of the object measured within its frame of reference.

This expression shows that the mass of an object tends towards infinity as its speed approaches the speed of light. It is therefore impossible to accelerate an object beyond the speed of light – the maximum possible speed.

Progress check

1. A muon has a half-life of 2 microseconds, measured within its frame of reference. Calculate the observed half-life when the muon moves at 0.99c.
2. Explain why a moving spacecraft appears shorter but not narrower to an external observer.

2 Length contraction only occurs in the direction of motion.

1 14 microseconds

Sample question and model answer

In this question, take the value of g, free-fall acceleration, to be 10 m s^{-2}.

A toy vehicle, mass 60 g, is at rest at the foot of a slope.

A second vehicle, mass 90 g, which is moving at a speed of 1.20 m s^{-1} hits the back of the stationary vehicle and they stick together.

1.20 m s^{-1}

When objects stick together, there is always some energy transfer from kinetic energy to internal energy, as some deformation occurs.

(a) (i) What type of collision occurs?   [1]

> Inelastic   1 mark

However, total energy is always conserved, no matter what type of collision.

   (ii) Which of the following quantities are conserved in this collision?   [1]

                    kinetic energy   momentum   total energy

> Momentum and total energy.   1 mark

Always write down the formula that you intend to use, and each step in the working. Otherwise, a simple error such as using the wrong mass results in no marks.

(b) (i) Calculate the momentum of the larger vehicle before the collision.   [3]

> momentum = mass × velocity   1 mark
>   = 0.090 kg × 1.20 m s^{-1} 1 mark
>   = 0.108 kg m s^{-1} 1 mark

   (ii) Calculate the combined speed of the vehicles after the collision.   [3]

The first mark here is for correct transposition of the equation.

> velocity = momentum ÷ mass   1 mark
>   = 0.108 kg m s^{-1} ÷ 0.150 kg   1 mark
>   = 0.72 m s^{-1} 1 mark

The second mark is for using the correct values.

(c) Calculate the vertical height of the vehicles' centre of mass when they come to rest   on the slope.
    [5]

It is not essential to include the units at each stage of the calculation, but it is good practice and you MUST include the correct unit with your answer to each part.

> As the vehicles rise up the slope, kinetic energy is transferred to
> gravitational potential energy   1 mark
>
> $\frac{1}{2}$ mv^2 = mgΔh   1 mark
>
> Δh = v^2 ÷ 2g   1 mark
>   = (0.72 m s^{-1})^2 ÷ (2 × 10 m s^{-2})   1 mark
>   = 0.026 m   1 mark

Practice examination questions

Throughout this section, take the value of g, free fall acceleration, to be 10 m s^{-2}.

1

A child of mass 40 kg sits on a swing. An adult pulls the swing back, raising the child's centre of mass through a vertical height of 0.60 m. This is shown in the diagram.

(a) Calculate the increase in gravitational potential energy when the child moves from position B to position A. [3]

(b) The child is released from position A.
Calculate her speed as she passes through position B. [3]

(c) Explain why there must be a resultant (unbalanced) force on the child as she swings through position B and state the direction of this force. [2]

(d) Calculate the size of the resultant force that acts on the child as she swings through position B. [3]

(e) One force that acts on the child at position B is the upward push of the swing.
Write a description of the other force that acts on the child. [2]

(f) Write down the value of the upward push of the swing when the child is:
(i) stationary at B.
(ii) moving through B. [2]

2

The diagram shows two 'vehicles' on an air track approaching each other. After impact they stick together.

Practice examination questions *(continued)*

(a) Calculate the total momentum of the vehicles before the collision. [3]

(b) Calculate the velocity of the vehicles after the collision. State the direction of motion. [3]

(c) By performing appropriate calculations, explain whether the collision is elastic or inelastic. [3]

3

A communications satellite in a geostationary orbit (orbit time = 24 hours) goes round the Earth at a distance of 4.24×10^7 m from the centre of the Earth.

(a) Calculate the orbital speed of the communications satellite. [3]

(b) Calculate the centripetal acceleration of the satellite and state its direction. [4]

(c) What force causes this acceleration? [2]

4

A tennis ball has a mass of 60 g. A ball travelling at a speed of 15 m s^{-1} hits a player's racket and rebounds with a speed of 24 m s^{-1}. The ball is in contact with the racket for a time of 12 ms.

(a) Calculate the change in momentum of the ball. [3]

(b) Calculate the average force exerted by the racket on the ball. [4]

(c) Calculate the average force exerted by the ball on the racket. [1]

(d) Describe the energy transfers that take place while the ball is in contact with the racket. [3]

5

The diagram shows a tractor being used to pull a log.

The tension in the steel rope is 600 N.

(a) Calculate the horizontal component of the forwards force on the log. [2]

(b) What other horizontal force acts on the log and what is the size of this force? [2]

(c) Calculate the work done on the log when it is pulled a distance of 250 m. [3]

(d) What happens to the energy used to pull the log? [2]

Practice examination questions (continued)

6

A car of mass 800 kg travels around a circular corner of radius 100 m at a speed of 14 m s^{-1}.

(a) Calculate the centripetal acceleration of the car. [3]

(b) Calculate the size of the force needed to cause this acceleration. [3]

(c) (i) Write a description of the force that causes this acceleration. [2]

    (ii) What is the other force that makes up the pair of forces in the sense of Newton's third law? [2]

(d) Suggest why, in wet or icy conditions, cars sometimes leave the road when travelling round a bend. [2]

7

A jet aircraft has a mass of 500 000 kg when fully laden.
It accelerates from rest to a take-off speed of 60 m s^{-1} in 20 s.

(a) Calculate the momentum of the aircraft as it leaves the ground. [2]

(b) Calculate the mean force required to impart this momentum to the aircraft. [2]

(c) Suggest why the force produced by the engines during take-off is greater than the answer to (b). [2]

(d) How does the principle of conservation of momentum apply to this event? [2]

8

In a hydroelectric power station, water falls at the rate of 3.2×10^5 kg s^{-1} through a vertical height of 180 m before entering a turbine.

(a) Calculate the loss in gravitational potential energy of the water each second. [3]

(b) Assuming that all this energy is transferred to kinetic energy, calculate the speed of the water as it enters the turbines. [3]

(c) The water leaves the turbines at a speed of 3 m s^{-1}. Calculate the maximum energy transfer to the turbine each second. [2]

9

(a) Explain the meaning of the expression *natural frequency of vibration*. [2]

(b) In what circumstances does an object resonate? [2]

(c) The speed of sound in air is 340 m s^{-1}.

Sound waves with a wavelength of 0.15 m cause a glass tumbler to vibrate at its natural frequency.

Calculate the natural frequency of vibration of the tumbler. [3]

10

A mass is suspended on a spring. After it is given a small displacement its equation of motion is:

$$a = -kx/m$$

(a) State the meaning of the symbols used in this equation. [4]

(b) The diagram shows how the displacement of the mass changes during one cycle of oscillation.

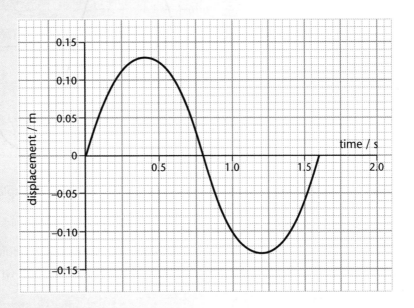

Calculate:

    (i) the amplitude of the oscillation [1]

    (ii) the frequency of the oscillation. [2]

(c) The mass on the spring is 0.50 kg. Calculate the spring constant. [3]

(d) (i) Calculate the maximum kinetic energy of the mass. [3]

    (ii) At what point on its motion does the mass have its maximum kinetic energy? [1]

11

The graph shows how the displacement of a pendulum bob changes over one cycle of its motion.

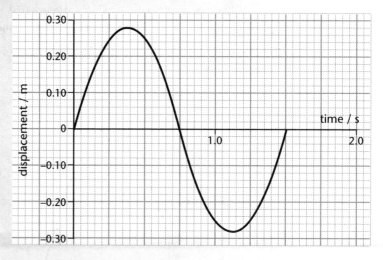

The equation that represents the variation of displacement with time is $x = A \sin 2\pi ft$.

(a) Write down the values of A and f. [2]

(b) Calculate the maximum velocity of the pendulum bob. [1]

(c) Calculate the velocity of the pendulum bob when its displacement is 0.20 m. [2]

Chapter 2

Fields

The following topics are covered in this chapter:

- *Gravitational fields*
- *Electric fields*
- *Capacitors and exponential change*

- *Magnetic fields*
- *Circular orbits*
- *Electromagnetic induction*

2.1 Gravitational fields

After studying this section you should be able to:

- *understand the concept of a field*
- *recall and use the relationship that describes the gravitational force between two masses*
- *describe the Earth's gravitational field and explain how the field strength varies with distance from the centre of the Earth*
- *understand gravitational field strength and gravitational potential as properties of points in the field*

LEARNING SUMMARY

Fields

AQA A	4	Edexcel context	5
AQA B	4	OCR A	G484
CCEA	A2.2	OCR B	G494
Edexcel concept	5	WJEC	4

A field is a region of space where forces are exerted on objects with certain properties. In this and subsequent sections three types of field are considered:

- **gravitational fields** affect anything that has mass

- **electric fields** affect anything that has charge

- **magnetic fields** affect moving charge such as the electrons in the atoms of permanent magnets and electric currents.

These three types of field have many similar properties and some important differences. There are key definitions and concepts that are common to all three types of field.

Gravitational fields

AQA A	4	Edexcel context	5
AQA B	4	OCR A	G484
CCEA	A2.2	OCR B	G494
Edexcel concept	5	WJEC	4

Newton realised that all objects with mass attract each other. This seems surprising, since any two objects placed close together on a desktop do not immediately move together. The attractive force between them is tiny, and very much smaller than the frictional forces that oppose their motion.

Gravitational attractive forces between two objects only affect their motion when at least one of the objects is very massive. This explains why we are aware of the force that attracts us and other objects towards the Earth – the Earth is very massive.

> The mass of the Earth is about 6×10^{24} kg.

The diagram represents the Earth's gravitational field. The lines show the direction of the force that acts on a mass that is within the field. Such lines are called field lines or lines of force.

This diagram shows that:

- gravitational forces are always attractive – the Earth cannot repel any objects
- the Earth's gravitational pull acts towards the centre of the Earth
- the Earth's gravitational field is radial; the field lines become less concentrated with increasing distance from the Earth.

The less concentrated the field lines, the smaller the force. The force exerted on an object in a gravitational field depends on its position. If the **gravitational field strength** at any point is known, then the size of the force on a particular mass can be calculated.

> Gravitational field strength is a vector quantity: its direction is towards the object that causes the field.

> Always use the given value for g. Candidates can lose marks for using $10\,\text{m}\,\text{s}^{-2}$ if the formula sheet gives $g = 9.81\,\text{m}\,\text{s}^{-2}$.

> **KEY POINT**
>
> The gravitational field strength (g) at any point in a gravitational field is *the force per unit mass* at that point:
> $$g = F/m$$
> Close to the Earth's surface, g has the value of $9.81\,\text{N}\,\text{kg}^{-1}$, though the value of $10\,\text{N}\,\text{kg}^{-1}$ is often used in calculations.

Universal gravitation

AQA A	4	Edexcel context	5
AQA B	4	OCR A	G484
CCEA	A2.2	OCR B	G494
Edexcel concept	5	WJEC	4

In studying gravitation, Newton concluded that the gravitational attractive force that exists between any two masses:

- is proportional to each of the masses
- is inversely proportional to the square of their distances apart.

> A point mass is one that has a radial field, like that of the Earth.

> **KEY POINT**
>
> **Newton's law of gravitation** describes the gravitational force between two point masses. It can be written as:
> $$F = \frac{Gm_1 m_2}{r^2}$$
> where G is the universal gravitational constant and has the value
> $$6.7 \times 10^{-11}\,\text{N}\,\text{m}^2\,\text{kg}^{-2}$$
> and m_1 and m_2 are the values of the masses, and r is the separation of the centres of mass.

> Remember that two objects attract *each other* with equal-sized forces acting in opposite directions as expected from Newton's third law.

Although the Earth is a large object, on the scale of the Universe it can be considered to be a point mass. The gravitational field strength at its centre is zero, since attractive forces pull equally in all directions. Beyond the surface of the Earth, the gravitational force on an object decreases with increasing distance. When the distance is measured from the centre of the Earth, the size of the force follows an **inverse square law**; doubling the distance from the centre of the Earth decreases the force to one quarter of the original value. The variation of force with distance from the centre of the Earth is shown in the diagram.

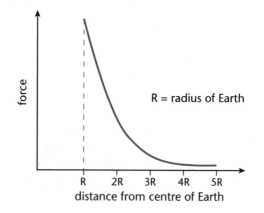

52

g and G

Newton's law of gravitation can be used to work out the value of the force between any two objects. It can also be used to calculate the strength of the gravitational field due to a spherical mass such as the Earth or the Sun.

> **KEY POINT**
>
> A small object, mass m, placed within the gravitational field of the Earth, mass M, experiences a force, F, given by
>
> $$F = \frac{GMm}{r^2}$$
>
> where r is the separation of the centres of mass of the object and the Earth.

A negative sign is sometimes used on the right-hand side of this equation, following the convention that attractive forces are given negative values and repulsive forces positive values.

It follows from the definition of gravitational field strength as the *force per unit mass* that the field strength at a point, g, is related to the mass of the Earth by the expression:

> **KEY POINT**
>
> $$g = \frac{F}{m} = \frac{GM}{r^2}$$

Gravitational field strength is a property of any point in a field. It can be given a value whether or not a mass is placed at that point. Like gravitational force, beyond the surface of the Earth the value of g follows an inverse square law. A graph of g against distance from the centre of the Earth has the same shape as that shown in the graph on page 52.

The radius of the Earth is about 6.4×10^6 m, so you would have to go much higher than aircraft-flying height for g to change by 1%.

Because the inverse square law applies to values of g when the distance is measured from the centre of the Earth, there is little change in its value close to the Earth's surface. Even when flying in an aircraft at a height of 10 000 m, the change in distance from the centre of the Earth is minimal, so there is no noticeable change in g.

The same symbol, g, is used to represent:

* gravitational field strength
* free-fall acceleration.

Gravitational field strength, g, is defined as the force per unit mass, g = F/m. From Newton's second law and the definition of the newton, free-fall acceleration, g, is also equal to the gravitational force per unit mass. The units of gravitational field strength, N kg^{-1}, and free-fall acceleration, m s^{-2}, are also equivalent.

Potential and potential energy

When an object changes its position relative to the Earth, there is a change in potential energy given by $\Delta E_p = mg\Delta h$. Δh is the change in height. It is not possible to place an absolute value on the potential energy of any object when h is measured relative to the surface of the Earth. Two similar objects placed at the top and bottom of a hill have different values of potential energy, but relative to the ground immediately around them the potential energy is zero for both objects, see diagram on the next page.

Absolute values of potential energy are measured relative to infinity. In this context, infinity means 'at a distance from the Earth where its gravitational field strength is so small as to be negligible'.

The car at the top of the hill has more potential energy than the one at the bottom, but relative to local ground level they both have zero.

The cars would only have zero potential energy if an infinite distance from the Earth or any other object. Using the ground as the starting point we can only calculate *changes* in potential energy.

Work has to be done to move an object from within the Earth's gravitational field to infinity.

Using infinity as the reference point:

• all objects at infinity have the same amount of potential energy, zero

• any object closer than infinity has a negative amount of potential energy, since it would need to acquire energy in order to reach infinity and have zero energy.

Just as every point in a gravitational field has a value of gravitational field strength, whether or not there is any body at that point, every point has a **gravitational potential**.

> **KEY POINT**
>
> The gravitational potential at a point in a gravitational field is the potential energy per unit mass placed at that point, measured relative to infinity.

So if the potential at any point in a field is known, the potential energy of a mass placed at that point can be calculated by multiplying the potential by the mass.

Calculating potential and potential energy

AQA A	4
AQA B	4
OCR B	G494
WJEC	4

The centre of mass of a planet is normally taken to be at its centre.

When an object is within the gravitational field of a planet, it has a negative amount of potential energy measured relative to infinity. The amount of potential energy depends on:

• the mass of the object

• the mass of the planet

• the distance between the centres of mass of the object and the planet.

> **KEY POINT**
>
> The gravitational potential energy measured relative to infinity of a mass, m, placed within the gravitational field of a spherical mass M can be calculated using:
>
> $$E_p = -\frac{GMm}{r}$$
>
> where r is the distance between the centres of mass and G is the universal gravitational constant.
>
> Gravitational potential energy is measured in joules (J).

Since gravitational potential is the gravitational potential energy per unit mass placed at a point in a field, it follows that:

> **KEY POINT**
>
> Gravitational potential, V, is given by the relationship:
>
> $$V = \frac{E_p}{m} = -\frac{GM}{r}$$
>
> Gravitational potential is measured in J kg⁻¹.

The relationship between potential and potential energy is similar to that between gravitational force and gravitational field strength:

- potential and field strength are properties of a point in a field
- potential energy and force are the corresponding quantities for of a mass placed within a field.

Equipotential surfaces

For a satellite in an elliptical orbit, there is an interchange between kinetic and potential energy as it travels around the Earth.

The potential energy of a satellite in a circular orbit around the Earth remains constant provided that its distance from the centre of the Earth does not change. To move to a higher or lower orbit the satellite must gain or lose potential energy. The satellite travels along an **equipotential surface**, the spherical shape consisting of points all at the same potential.

The diagram shows the spacing of equipotential surfaces around the Earth. The surfaces are drawn at equal differences of potential.

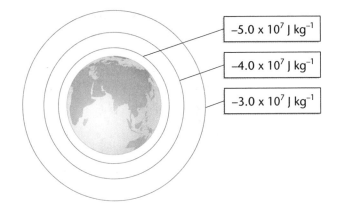

-5.0×10^7 J kg^{-1}

-4.0×10^7 J kg^{-1}

-3.0×10^7 J kg^{-1}

The diagram shows that:

- equipotential surfaces around a spherical mass are also spherical
- the spacing between the equipotential surfaces increases with increasing distance from the centre of the Earth.

To move to a lower orbit, a rocket can lose energy by firing the rocket engines 'backwards' so that the exhaust gases are expelled in the direction of motion.

For a **satellite** to move from an orbit where the potential is -4.0×10^7 J kg^{-1} to one where the potential is -3.0×10^7 J kg^{-1}, it needs to gain 1.0×10^7 J of gravitational potential energy for each kilogram of satellite. It does this by firing the rocket engines, transferring energy from its fuel supply.

Potential gradient

The graph shows that the rate of change of potential with distance, the potential gradient, decreases with increasing distance from the Earth.

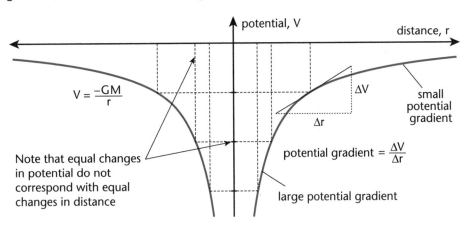

potential, V

distance, r

$$V = \frac{-GM}{r}$$

ΔV

small potential gradient

Δr

potential gradient $= \dfrac{\Delta V}{\Delta r}$

Note that equal changes in potential do not correspond with equal changes in distance

large potential gradient

As the potential gradient decreases, so does the gravitational field strength.

The concept of potential gradient is similar to that of the gradient of a hill or slope. The steeper the slope, the greater the acceleration of an object free to move down it.

The relationship between gravitational field strength and potential gradient is:

$$g = -\text{(potential gradient)} \text{ or } g = -\frac{\Delta V}{\Delta r}$$

where ΔV is the change in potential over a small distance Δr.

Progress check

1 The radius of the Earth is 6.4×10^6 m and the gravitational field strength at its surface is 10 N kg^{-1}.
   At what height above the surface of the Earth is the gravitational field strength equal to 2.5 N kg^{-1}?

2 Two 2.5 kg masses are placed with their centres 10 cm apart.
   Calculate the size of the gravitational attractive force between them.
   $G = 6.7 \times 10^{-11}$ N m^2 kg^{-2}.

3 The mass of the Moon is 7.4×10^{22} kg and its radius is 1.7×10^6 m.
   Using the value of G from Q2, calculate the value of free-fall acceleration at the Moon's surface.

3 1.7 m s^{-2}
2 4.2×10^{-8} N
1 6.4×10^6 m

2.2 Electric fields

After studying this section you should be able to:

- *describe the electric field due to a point charge and between two charged parallel plates*
- *calculate the force on a charge in an electric field*
- *compare gravitational and electric fields*
- *understand electric field strength and electric potential as properties of points in the field*

Charging up

AQA A	4	Edexcel context	4
AQA B	5	OCR A	G485
CCEA	A2.2	OCR B	G495
Edexcel concept	4	WJEC	4

Electrostatic phenomena are due to the forces between charged objects. Similar charges repel and opposite charges attract.

Transfer of charge between two objects can happen when they slide relative to each other. It is caused by electrons leaving one surface and joining the other. This results in objects having one of two types of charge:

- an object that gains electrons has a negative charge
- an object that loses electrons has a positive charge.

In many cases any imbalance of charge on an object is removed by movement of electrons to or from the ground, but if at least one of the objects is a good insulator charge can build up.

A balloon is easily charged by rubbing but it is not possible to charge a hand-held metal rod since it is immediately discharged by exchange of electrons with the person holding it.

The **quantum**, or smallest unit, of charge is that carried by an electron. All quantities of charge must be a whole number multiple of $e = -1.6 \times 10^{-19}$ C.

The electric field

AQA A	4	Edexcel context	4
AQA B	5	OCR A	G485
CCEA	A2.2	OCR B	G495
Edexcel concept	4	WJEC	4

Unlike gravitational fields, where there are only attractive forces, electric fields can give rise to attraction or repulsion of objects that are charged. When drawing field lines that represent the forces due to a charged object, the arrows show the direction of the force on a positive charge.

The diagram shows the electric fields due to a 'point charge' and between a pair of oppositely charged parallel plates.

A pair of parallel plates become oppositely charged when connected to the positive and negative terminals of a d.c. supply.

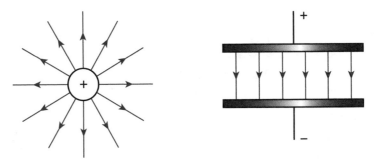

The field due to the point charge is radial, it decreases in strength with increasing distance from the charge. That between the parallel plates is uniform, it maintains a constant strength at all points between the plates.

The size of the force between two point charges is:

- proportional to each of the charges
- inversely proportional to the square of their distances apart.

Compare this equation with that for gravitational force.

Permittivity is a measure of the extent to which the medium reinforces the electric field. Water has a high permittivity due to its molecules being polarised.

Coulomb's law states that the force between two point charges is given by

$$F = \frac{kQ_1 Q_2}{r^2}$$

where Q_1 and Q_2 represent the values of the charges, r is their distance apart and k has the value, in air or a vacuum, of $\frac{1}{4\pi\varepsilon_0} = 9.0 \times 10^9$ N m^2 C^{-2}.

The constant ε_0 is called the permittivity of free space.

Field strength

AQA A	4	Edexcel context	4
AQA B	5	OCR A	G485
CCEA	A2.2	OCR B	G495
Edexcel concept	4	WJEC	4

The test charge has to be small enough to have no effect on the field.

Electric field strength of a point:

- is defined *as the force per unit positive charge that would act if a small charge were placed at that point*
- is measured in N C^{-1}.

Coulomb's law can be used to express the field strength due to a point charge Q. Since the force between a charge Q and a small charge q placed within the field of Q is given by $F = \frac{kQq}{r^2}$, it follows that:

Compare the equations for electric field strength and gravitational field strength.

The electric field strength, E, due to a point charge Q is given by the expression:

$$E = \frac{F}{q} = \frac{kQ}{r^2}$$

In a radial field, the field strength follows an inverse square law. This can be seen by the way in which the field lines spread out from a point charge. In a uniform field, like the one between two oppositely charged parallel plates, the field lines maintain a constant separation. The value of the electric field strength in a uniform field is the same at all points.

This gives an alternative unit for electric field strength, V m^{-1}, which is equivalent to the N C^{-1}.

The electric field strength between two oppositely charged parallel plates is given by the expression:

$$E = \frac{V}{d}$$

where V is the potential difference between the plates and d is the separation of the plates.

Potential in a radial field

AQA A	4	Edexcel context	4
AQA B	5	OCR A	G485
CCEA	A2.2	OCR B	G495
Edexcel concept	4	WJEC	4

Unlike the potential in the gravitational field of a point mass, the electric potential in the field of a point charge is positive, since work has to be done to move a positive charge from infinity to any point in the field.

Like potential in a gravitational field, absolute potential in an electric field is measured relative to infinity.

The electric potential at a point, V, is the work done per unit positive charge in bringing a small charge from infinity to that point.

In a radial field, $$V = \frac{1}{4\pi\varepsilon_0} \frac{Q}{r}$$

The unit of electric potential is the joule per coulomb, also known as a volt.

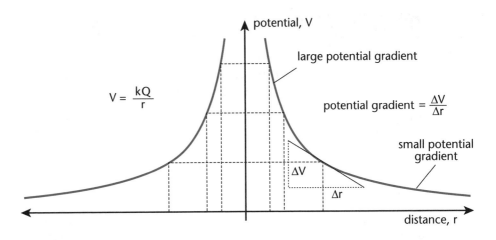

$$V = \frac{kQ}{r}$$

potential, V

large potential gradient

$$\text{potential gradient} = \frac{\Delta V}{\Delta r}$$

small potential gradient

ΔV

Δr

distance, r

Potential and potential difference

AQA A	4	Edexcel context	4
AQA B	5	OCR A	G485
CCEA	A2.2	OCR B	G495
Edexcel concept	4	WJEC	4

In a uniform field the potential changes by equal amounts for equal changes in distance.

The diagram here shows the variation in potential between two oppositely charged plates.

In this example:

> Potential could be measured relative to the upper plate, in which case the potentials would have negative values.

- potential has been measured relative to the lower plate, which has been given the value 0
- the equipotential lines are parallel to the plates
- an equipotential surface, joining points all at the same potential, is simply a surface drawn parallel to the plates.

+200 V

+150 V
+100 V
+50 V

0 V

+200V

0V

d

The potential difference between any two points is just that – a difference in potential between them. The potential difference between the parallel plates represents the energy transfer per coulomb when charge moves between them. A charge, q, moving between the plates would gain or lose energy Vq.

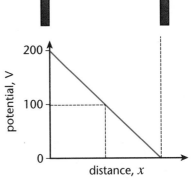

$$\text{potential gradient} = \frac{\Delta V}{\Delta x} = \frac{V}{d}$$

where d is the separation of the plates and V is the potential difference between them (200 V in this diagram)

Electron beams

AQA A	4	Edexcel context	4
AQA B	5	OCR A	G485
CCEA	A2.2	OCR B	G495
Edexcel concept	4	WJEC	4

The filament is the cathode, or negative terminal. The anode is usually cylindrical and is connected to the positive terminal of the high voltage supply.

Note that there is a potential difference (a difference in potential) between the anode and the cathode. Here, this difference in potential is marked as a 'high voltage'.

When the electron is accelerated between two points which have a difference of potential of 1 volt between them, then the energy it gains is 1.6×10^{-19} J, which is also called one electron-volt, or 1eV.

Cathode ray oscilloscopes use beams of electrons. The beam is produced by an electron gun, a device that accelerates and focuses the electrons given off by a hot wire. The diagram below shows an electron gun.

An electron gun

The low voltage supply heats the filament, causing it to emit electrons. The electrons are accelerated by the high voltage supply, gaining kinetic energy as they move towards the positively charged anode. Since the potential difference between the cathode and the anode represents the energy transfer per coulomb of charge, the kinetic energy of the accelerated electrons can be calculated.

> **KEY POINT**
>
> When an electron is accelerated through a potential difference, V, it gains kinetic energy
>
> $$\frac{1}{2} m_e v^2 = eV$$
>
> where m_e is the mass of an electron and e is the electron charge.

Deflecting a beam of electrons

AQA A	4	Edexcel context	4
AQA B	5	OCR A	G485
CCEA	A2.2	OCR B	G495
Edexcel concept	4	WJEC	4

In a cathode ray oscilloscope, vertical deflection of the electron beam is achieved by passing the beam between a pair of oppositely charged parallel plates. The effect of this can be seen by studying the path of a beam of electrons in a deflection tube.

When passing between the plates, the electrons have a constant speed in the direction parallel to the plates. Perpendicular to the plates, the force on each electron is equal to Ee (where E is the electric field strength), so they accelerate in this direction. The consequent motion of the electrons is similar to that of a body such as a stone projected horizontally on the Earth; in each case the result is a parabolic path, shown in the diagram.

The path of the electrons before entering the field and after leaving the field is a straight line as there is no resultant force acting on them.

When moving between the plates:

- the electrons travel equal distances in successive equal time intervals in the direction parallel to the plates
- the electrons travel increasing distances in successive equal time intervals in the direction perpendicular to the plates.

Comparing electric and gravitational fields

AQA A	4	OCR A	G48S
AQA B	5	OCR B	G49S
Edexcel concept	5	WJEC	4
Edexcel context	5		

There are similarities and differences between electric and gravitational fields:

- electric field strength is defined as force per unit charge, gravitational field strength is defined as force per unit mass
- electric potential and gravitational potential are defined in similar ways
- the electric field due to a point charge is similar to the gravitational field of a point mass and the inverse square law applies in both cases
- electric fields can attract or repel charged objects, gravitational fields can only attract masses.
- the values of G (the universal gravitational constant) and $1/4\pi\varepsilon_0$ where ε_0 is the permittivity of a vacuum) are a very different, so gravitational forces and electric forces dominate at different scales in nature.

Progress check

1 Calculate the electric field strength due to a point charge of 3.0 μC at a distance of 0.10 m from the charge.
$$\frac{1}{4\pi\varepsilon_0} = 9.0 \times 10^9 \text{ N m}^2 \text{ C}^{-2}$$

2 The potential difference between two parallel plates is 300 V. They are placed 0.15 m apart.
   a Calculate the value of the electric field strength between the plates.
   b Calculate the size of the force on an electron, charge -1.6×10^{-19} C, placed midway between the plates.
   c Explain how the size of the force on the electron varies as it moves from the negative plate to the positive plate.

c It stays the same as the field strength does not vary.
b 3.2×10^{-16} N
2 a 2.0×10^3 N C^{-1}
1 2.7×10^6 N C^{-1}

2.3 Capacitors and exponential change

After studying this section you should be able to:

- describe the action of a capacitor and calculate the charge stored
- relate the energy stored in a capacitor to a graph of charge against voltage
- explain the significance of the time constant of a circuit that contains a capacitor and a resistor

LEARNING SUMMARY

The action of a capacitor

AQA A	4	Edexcel context	4
AQA B	5	OCR A	G485
CCEA	A2.2	OCR B	G495
Edexcel concept	4	WJEC	5

Capacitors store charge and energy. They have many applications, including smoothing varying direct currents, electronic timing circuits and powering the memory to store information in calculators when they are switched off.

A capacitor consists of two parallel conducting plates separated by an insulator. When it is connected to a voltage supply, charge flows onto the capacitor plates until the potential difference across them is the same as that of the supply. The charge flow and the final charge on each plate is shown in the diagram.

> When a capacitor is charging, charge flows in all parts of the circuit except between the plates.

As the capacitor charges:

- charge $-Q$ flows onto the plate connected to the negative terminal of the supply
- charge $-Q$ flows off the plate connected to the positive terminal of the supply, leaving it with charge $+Q$
- the capacitor plates always have the same quantity of charge, but of the opposite sign
- no charge flows between the plates of the capacitor.

Capacitance

AQA A	4	Edexcel context	4
AQA B	5	OCR A	G485
CCEA	A2.2	OCR B	G495
Edexcel concept	4	WJEC	5

The capacitor shown in the diagram above is said to store charge Q, meaning that this is the amount of charge on each plate.

When a capacitor is charged, the amount of charge stored depends on:

- the voltage across the capacitor
- its capacitance, i.e. the greater the capacitance, the more charge is stored at a given voltage.

> As the capacitor plates have equal amounts of charge of the opposite sign, the total charge is actually zero.
>
> However, because the charges are separated they have energy and can do work when they are brought together.

> **The capacitance of a capacitor, C, is defined as:**
>
> $$C = \frac{Q}{V}$$
>
> Where Q is the charge stored when the voltage across the capacitor is V. Capacitance is measured in farads (F).
> 1 farad is the capacitance of a capacitor that stores 1 C of charge when the p.d. across it is 1 V.
>
> **KEY POINT**

One farad is a very large value of capacitance. Common values of capacitance are usually measured in picofarads (1 pF $= 1.0 \times 10^{-12}$ F) and microfarads (1 µF $= 1.0 \times 10^{-6}$ F).

Combining capacitors

AQA A	4
CCEA	A2.2
WJEC	5

The effect of adding capacitors in series is to reduce the capacitance. When an additional capacitor is added, there is less p.d. across each one so less charge is stored.

Like resistors, capacitors can be connected in **series** or **parallel** to achieve different values of capacitance.

When capacitors in series are connected to a voltage supply:

* no matter what the value of its capacitance, each capacitor in the combination stores the same amount of charge, since any one plate can only lose or gain the charge gained or lost by the plate that it is connected to
* the total charge stored by a series combination is the charge on each of the two outer plates and is equal to the charge stored on each individual capacitor
* because the applied potential difference is shared by the capacitors, the total charge stored is less than the charge that would be stored by any one of the capacitors connected individually to the voltage supply.

The diagram shows the charge on the plates of three capacitors connected in series.

This results in the effective value of a series combination of capacitors being smaller than the lowest value capacitor in the combination.

A common error when using this relationship is to forget to carry out the final reciprocation, giving an answer which is equal to $\frac{1}{C}$ instead of C.

> **KEY POINT**
>
> The capacitance, C, of a number of capacitors connected in series is given by the expression:
> $$\frac{1}{C} = \frac{1}{C_1} + \frac{1}{C_2} + \frac{1}{C_3}$$

In contrast to this, the effect of connecting capacitors in parallel is to increase the capacitance so that the effective value of a number of capacitors in parallel is always greater than the largest value of the combination.

When capacitors are connected in parallel:

* all the capacitors are charged to the same potential difference
* each capacitor stores the same amount of charge as it would if connected on its own to the same voltage
* adding an additional capacitor increases the total charge stored.

The expressions for capacitors connected in series and parallel are similar to those for resistors, but the other way round.

> **KEY POINT**
>
> The capacitance, C, of a number of capacitors connected in parallel is given by the expression:
> $$C = C_1 + C_2 + C_3$$

The energy stored in a capacitor

AQA A	4	Edexcel context	4
AQA B	5	OCR A	G485
CCEA	A2.2	OCR B	G495
Edexcel concept	4	WJEC	5

Energy is needed from a power supply or other source to charge a capacitor.

A charged capacitor can supply the energy needed to maintain the memory in a calculator or the current in a circuit when the supply voltage is too low.

The amount of energy stored in a capacitor depends on:

- the amount of charge on the capacitor plates
- the voltage required to place this charge on the capacitor plates, i.e. the capacitance of the capacitor.

The graph below shows how the voltage across the plates of a capacitor depends on the charge stored.

> When a charge ΔQ is added to a capacitor at a potential difference V, the work done is ΔQV. The total work done in charging a capacitor is $\Sigma \Delta QV$.

voltage, V

charge stored, Q

The shaded area between the graph line and the charge axis represents the energy stored in the capacitor.

> **KEY POINT**
>
> The energy, E, stored in a capacitor is given by the expression
>
> $$E = \frac{1}{2}QV = \frac{1}{2}CV^2$$
>
> where Q is the charge stored on a capacitor of capacitance C when the voltage across it is V.

Charging and discharging a capacitor

AQA A	4	Edexcel context	4
AQA B	5	OCR A	G485
CCEA	A2.2	OCR B	G495
Edexcel concept	4	WJEC	5

> Having a resistor in the circuit means that extra work has to be done to charge the capacitor, as there is always an energy transfer to heat when charge flows through a resistor.

> **Key points from AS**
>
> - **The relationship between resistance, current and voltage.**
>   *Revise AS section 2.1*

When a capacitor is charged by connecting it directly to a power supply, there is very little resistance in the circuit and the capacitor seems to charge instantaneously. This is because the process occurs over a very short time interval. Placing a resistor in the charging circuit reduces the rate of flow of charge (current) and slows the process down. The greater the values of resistance and capacitance, the longer it takes for the capacitor to charge.

The diagram below shows how the current changes with time when a capacitor is charging through a resistor.

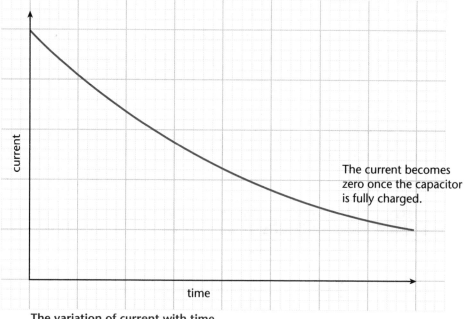

current

time

The current becomes zero once the capacitor is fully charged.

The variation of current with time when a capacitor is charging

As the p.d. across the capacitor rises, that across the resistor falls, reducing the current.

This graph shows that:

- the charging current falls as the charge on the capacitor, and the voltage across the capacitor, rise
- the charging current decreases by the same proportion in equal time intervals.

The second bullet point shows that the change in the current follows the same pattern as the activity of a radioactive isotope. This is an example of an **exponential change**. The charging current decreases exponentially.

Whenever the rate of change of any quantity, such as current, is proportional to the quantity itself, then the quantity changes exponentially.

The graph shown on the previous page can be used to work out the amount of charge that flows onto the capacitor by estimating the area between the graph line and the time axis. Since *current = rate of flow of charge* it follows that:

> On a graph of current against time, the area between the graph line and the time axis represents the charge flow.
>
> **KEY POINT**

Key points from AS

- **The relationship between current and charge flow.** *Revise AS section 2.2*

To calculate the charge flow:

- estimate the number of whole squares between the graph line and the time axis
- multiply this by the 'charge value' of each square, obtained by calculating $\Delta Q \times \Delta t$ for a single square.

The time constant

AQA A	4	Edexcel context	4
AQA B	5	OCR A	G485
CCEA	A2.2	OCR B	G495
Edexcel concept	4	WJEC	5

When a capacitor is charging or discharging, the amount of charge on the capacitor changes exponentially. The graphs in the diagram show how the charge on a capacitor changes with time when it is charging and discharging.

Graphs showing the change of voltage with time are the same shape.
Since $V = \dfrac{Q}{C}$, it follows that the only difference between a charge–time graph and a voltage–time graph is the label and scale on the *y*-axis.

These graphs show the charge on the capacitor approaching a final value, zero in the case of the capacitor discharging.

The charge on a capacitor during charging and discharging

The rate at which the charge on a capacitor changes depends on the **time constant** of the charging or discharging circuit.

> The time constant, t, of a capacitor charge or discharge circuit is the product of the resistance and the capacitance:
>
> $$t = RC$$
>
> t is measured in s.
>
> **KEY POINT**

The greater the values of R and C the longer the charge or discharge process takes. Knowledge of the values of R and C enables the amount of charge on a capacitor to be calculated at any time after the capacitor has started to charge or discharge. This is useful in timing circuits, where a switch is triggered once the charge, and therefore p.d., has reached a certain value.

e is a constant that has a value of 2.72 to 2 d.p. It is the base of the natural log and exponential functions.

The exponential function e is used to calculate the charge remaining on a capacitor that is discharging.

> **KEY POINT**
>
> The charge, Q, on a capacitor of capacitance C, remaining time t after starting to discharge is given by the expression
>
> $$Q = Q_0 e^{-t/RC}$$
>
> where Q_0 is the initial charge on the capacitor and RC is the time constant.

This expression shows that when t is equal to RC, i.e. after one time constant has elapsed, the charge remaining is equal to $Q_0 e^{-1}$, or $\frac{Q_0}{e}$

Progress check

1 The charge on a capacitor is 3.06×10^{-4} C when the p.d. across it is 6.5 V. Calculate the capacitance of the capacitor.

2 Three capacitors, of capacitance 2 μF, 3 μF and 6 μF, are connected together. Calculate the effective capacitance when they are connected:
   a in series
   b in parallel.

3 A 50 μF capacitor is charged to a p.d. of 360 V. Calculate the energy stored in the capacitor.

3 3.24 J
2 a 1 μF
   b 11 μF
1 4.71×10^{-5} F.

2.4 Magnetic fields

After studying this section you should be able to:

- describe the magnetic fields inside a solenoid and around a wire when current passes in them
- understand the meaning of magnetic field strength
- calculate the size and direction of the force that acts on a current in a magnetic field

LEARNING SUMMARY

Magnetic fields

AQA A	4	Edexcel context	4
AQA B	4	OCR A	G485
CCEA	A2.2	OCR B	G495
Edexcel concept	4	WJEC	5

> Although the field lines are often curves, the force at any point acts in a straight line.

Magnetic fields exist around *moving* charged bodies. In a permanent magnet the moving charges are within atoms that are aligned. In electric currents in wires the moving charges are electrons.

Likewise, *moving* charged bodies experience force when they are in magnetic fields. Charged bodies do not experience magnetic force if there is no relative motion relative to the field.

Like other fields, magnetic fields are represented by lines with arrows. The arrows show the direction of the force at any point in the field. The convention when drawing magnetic field lines is that the arrows show the direction of the force that would be exerted on the N-seeking pole of a permanent magnet placed at that point.

The diagrams show the field patterns around a bar magnet and between two different arrangements of pairs of magnets. Where equal-sized forces act in opposite directions, the result is a **neutral point**. At a neutral point, the resultant magnetic force is zero.

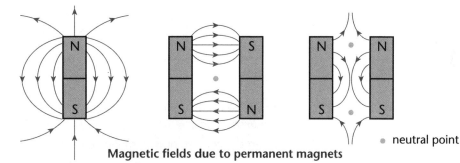

• neutral point

Magnetic fields due to permanent magnets

Magnetic field strength

AQA A	4	Edexcel context	4
AQA B	4	OCR A	G485
CCEA	A2.2	OCR B	G495
Edexcel concept	4	WJEC	5

In electric and gravitational fields, the strength of the field is defined in terms of the force per unit mass or charge. In magnetic fields the situation is a little more complicated, and both charge and its velocity relative to the field are involved. The size of a force on charge q moving with velocity v perpendicular to the field is given by $F = Bqv$. If we write $B = F/qv$ then this is analogous to $g = F/m$ in gravitational fields and $E = F/q$ in electric fields. B could then be called magnetic field strength, but in fact is normally called **magnetic flux density**. The unit of flux density is the tesla, T.

Magnetic field strength and the force on a wire

AQA A	4	Edexcel context	4
AQA B	4	OCR A	G485
CCEA	A2.2	OCR B	G495
Edexcel concept	4	WJEC	5

A current-carrying wire holds moving charges. In a magnetic field it experiences a force provided that it is not parallel to the field. 'Parallel to the field' means parallel to the field lines. The force has its maximum value when the current is

The force on any electric current that is parallel to a magnetic field is zero – there is no force.

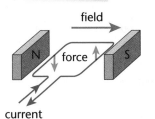

perpendicular to the field. **Fleming's left hand rule** shows the direction of the force on a current of positively charged bodies (or of conventional current) that has a component which is perpendicular to a magnetic field. The diagram, left, illustrates Fleming's rule and its application to a simple **motor**.

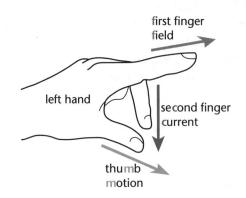

1 point your first finger in the direction of the magnetic field

2 point your second finger in the direction of the current

3 your thumb points in the direction of the resulting motion

Remember when using Fleming's rule that the current direction is conventional current, taken to be from + to –. The conventional current due to an electron flow is in the opposite direction to that of the electron movement. This arises because electric current was studied and conventions were established before electrons were discovered.

The size of the force on a current-carrying conductor in a magnetic field depends on:

- the size of the current
- the length of conductor in the field
- the orientation of the conductor relative to the field
- the strength of the magnetic field or flux density, B.

With the current and magnetic field directions shown in the diagram below the force is into the paper.

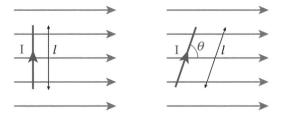

The force on a current-carrying conductor in a magnetic field is given by the expressions:

when the conductor is perpendicular to the field lines:

$$F = BIl$$

when the angle between the conductor and the field lines is θ,

$$F = BIl\sin\theta$$

KEY POINT

Fields due to currents

The diagram shows the magnetic field around a wire when a current passes in it.

The magnetic field pattern is a set of concentric circles around the wire. The change in the spacing of the circles shows that the magnetic field strength decreases with increasing distance from the wire. The magnetic field strength depends on:

- the size of the current
- the distance from the wire
- a constant called **permeability**, μ, which is a measure of the extent to which the surrounding medium reinforces the magnetic field.

Iron has a high permeability. This explains why a coil of wire wound on an iron core has a much greater magnetic field strength than a similar coil with an air core.

The symbol H represents the henry, a unit of electromagnetic induction.

> **KEY POINT**
>
> The magnetic field strength, B, due to a current, I, passing in a wire in a vacuum is given by the expression:
>
> $$B = \frac{\mu_0 I}{2\pi r}$$
>
> where μ_0 is the permeability of free space and has the value $4\pi \times 10^{-7}$ H m^{-1} and r is the distance from the wire.

The magnetic field pattern due to a current passing in a **solenoid** is shown in the diagram below.

On the outside of the solenoid, the field resembles that of a bar magnet. Inside, away from the ends of the solenoid, the parallel field lines show that the magnetic field strength is uniform.

The strength of this uniform field:

- is independent of the diameter of the solenoid
- depends on the number of turns of wire per metre of length, n.

> **KEY POINT**
>
> The magnetic field strength, B, inside a solenoid is given by the expression:
>
> $$B = \mu_0 nI$$
>
> where n is the number of turns of wire per metre, μ_0 is the permeability of free space and I is the current in the solenoid.

Progress check

1 Two parallel wires each carry a current in the same direction. Use Fleming's rule to determine whether the force between them is attractive or repulsive.

2 The magnetic field strength between two permanent magnets is 5.6×10^{-3} T. A wire carrying a current of 3.5 A is placed at right angles to their magnetic field. The length of wire within the field is 0.1 m. Calculate the size of the force on the wire.

3 An electron, charge -1.6×10^{-19} C, moves at a velocity of 2.4×10^7 m s^{-1} perpendicular to a magnetic field of strength 4.5×10^{-2} T. Calculate the size of the force on the electron.

3 1.73×10^{-13} N
2 1.96×10^{-3} N
1 Attractive.

2.5 Circular orbits

After studying this section you should be able to:

LEARNING SUMMARY

- *describe the forces acting on planets, moons and satellites*
- *explain how charged particles are accelerated in a cyclotron*

Movement in the Solar System

AQA A	4	Edexcel context	4
AQA B	4	OCR A	G485
Edexcel concept	5	WJEC	4

Mercury has a highly elliptical orbit. The other planets follow paths that are very close to being circles.

All planetary movement in the Solar System is anticlockwise, when viewed from above the North Pole. The further a planet is from the Sun, the slower the speed in its orbit. Although the orbits of the planets are ellipses, for most planets they are so close to circles that our understanding of circular motion can be applied.

Planets can then be considered to be:

- moving at constant speed in a circle around the Sun
- accelerating towards the Sun with centripetal acceleration v^2/r.

There are no resistive forces since the planets move through a vacuum. The only forces acting on them are gravitational. Gravitational attraction between a planet and the Sun provides the unbalanced force required to cause the centripetal acceleration.

The diagram shows the attractive forces between the Sun and a planet.

This diagram shows that the gravitational force on a planet acts at its centre of mass and is directed towards the Sun's centre of mass.

planet

Sun

The force on the planet is:

- equal in size and opposite in direction to that on the Sun
- at right angles to its direction of motion
- the unbalanced, centripetal force required to maintain circular motion.

Asteroids in the asteroid belt, between Mars and Jupiter, have a wide range of masses but similar orbit times.

By equating the gravitational force to centripetal force mv^2/r, it emerges that the orbital speed depends only on the orbital radius and not on the mass of the planet.

KEY POINT

The centripetal force required to keep a planet in a circular orbit is the gravitational force between the planet and the Sun:

$$\frac{M_p v^2}{r^2} = \frac{GM_s M_p}{r^2}$$

so where M_s is the mass of the Sun and M_p is the mass of the planet.

$$v^2 r = GM_s$$

Kepler's laws

CCEA — A2.2
OCR A — G485
WJEC — 4

Kepler's laws recognise the elliptical nature of planetary orbits.

Kepler's first law

The orbit of planets are ellipses, with the Sun at one focus of the ellipse.

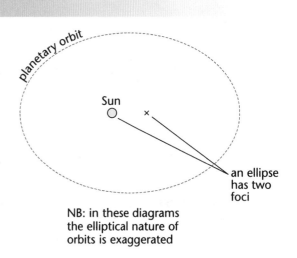

NB: in these diagrams the elliptical nature of orbits is exaggerated

It is worth noting that the orbit of the Earth, as for most planets, is elliptical motion with the two foci quite close together. So the orbit is not far from being circular.

However, with precise measurement, the prediction of position of planets in the sky is significantly affected by the elliptical nature of their orbits. The success of such predictions following the acceptance of the elliptical shapes led to relatively minor amendment to Copernicus' ideas about the Solar System and helped to confirm that his idea of the Sun at the centre was superior to the Earth-centred model.

Kepler's second law

The line between a planet and the Sun sweeps out equal areas in equal times.

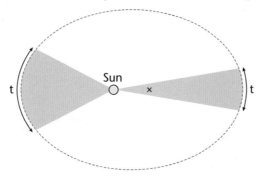

Note that a planet goes faster when closer to the Sun. Its total energy is constant, but when closer to the Sun it has higher kinetic energy and lower potential energy.

Kepler's third law

The square of the period of a planet is proportional to the cube of the 'radius'.

Note that planets further from the Sun have both greater radii and greater periods of orbit.

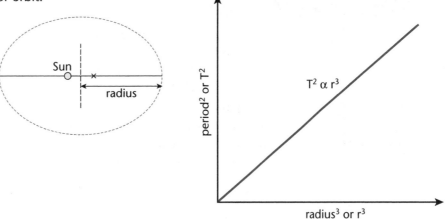

Artificial satellites

AQA A	4	Edexcel context	4
AQA B	4	OCR A	G484
CCEA	A2.2	WJEC	4
Edexcel concept	4		

The relationship between the orbital speed and radius of a planet can be applied to the orbit of a **satellite** around the Earth by replacing the mass of the Sun, M_s, with that of the Earth, M_E. This enables the speed of a satellite to be calculated at any orbital radius.

> The relationship also applies to the Earth's natural satellite, the Moon.

Some communications satellites occupy **geo-synchronous** orbits. A satellite in a geo-synchronous orbit:

- orbits above the equator
- remains in the same position relative to the Earth's surface
- has an orbit time of 24 hours.

The radius of a geo-synchronous orbit can be calculated from $v^2r = GM_E$, v can be written as $2\pi r/t$ to work out the value of r.

Circular orbits in magnetic fields

AQA A	4	Edexcel context	5
AQA B	5	WJEC	5
CCEA	A2.2		

When a charged particle moves at right angles to a magnetic field, the magnetic force on the particle is perpendicular to both its direction of motion and the magnetic field. This can result in circular motion.

The diagram shows the path and the force on an electron moving in a magnetic field directed into the paper.

> When applying Fleming's rule to electrons, remember that the direction of the current is opposite to that of the electrons' motion, since electrons are negatively charged.
>
> So for this diagram the second finger should point from right to left. The first finger represents the field and points down into the page. The thumb represents the direction of the magnetic force.

direction of orbiting electron

F = Bev

The field lines are perpendicular to the page, with arrows pointing down into the paper.

The electron follows a circular path, the magnetic force being the unbalanced force required to cause acceleration towards the centre of the circle. The radius of the circular path is proportional to the speed of the electron.

> For an electron, Q = e, so the relationship is
>
> $Be = \dfrac{mv}{r}$.

KEY POINT
When a charge Q moves in a circular path in a magnetic field of strength *B*:
$$BQv = \frac{mv^2}{r}$$
so $$BQ = \frac{mv}{r}$$

The cyclotron

AQA A	4	Edexcel context	4
AQA B	5	WJEC	5
CCEA	A2.2		

A **cyclotron** uses a magnetic field to force charged particles to move in a 'circular' path, and an electric field to accelerate them as they travel around the circle. As the charged particles accelerate, the increase in speed results in an increase in the radius of the circle, so they spiral outwards.

> Particles accelerated in a cyclotron are used to probe atomic nuclei and for treating some cancers.

A cyclotron consists of two D-shaped halves called **dees**. A magnetic field acting at right angles to the plane of the dees causes a beam of charged particles to follow a circular path. Particles such as protons and alpha particles are both suitable for use in cyclotrons.

The diagram shows the path of protons produced at the centre of the cyclotron.

source of protons

high frequency accelerating voltage

'dees'

high-speed proton beam

In a cyclotron:

- the near circular pathways are a result of a magnetic field acting perpendicularly to the cyclotron and the pathways
- the beam of charged particles is accelerated as it passes from one dee into the other
- this occurs because of the alternating electric field which changes polarity so that it attracts the particles as they enter a dee
- the frequency of the alternating voltage must be equal to the frequency of rotation of the particles
- the radius of orbit increases as the particles accelerate.

The frequency of rotation of the charged particles in a cyclotron matches that of the accelerating voltage. The value of the magnetic field strength must be adjusted to also match this frequency.

If the frequency of the accelerating voltage is fixed, each orbit takes the same time. With an increase in the radius of successive orbits, the particles travel increasing distances in a given time period i.e. faster.

> **KEY POINT**
>
> The frequency of rotation of a charged particle in a cyclotron, f, is related to the magnetic field strength, B, by the expression:
>
> $$f = \frac{BQ}{2\pi m}$$
>
> where Q is the charge on a particle of mass m.

Balanced electric and magnetic fields

AQA B	5	Edexcel context	4
CCEA	A2.2	OCR A	G485
Edexcel concept	4	WJEC	5

Orbital motion of one charge around another is possible in radial electric fields.

radial electric field

$-q$

Q

A charge moving in a uniform electric field follows a pathway that is the same as that of a mass moving without resistance in a uniform gravitational field.

A charge moving as shown between two plates, and a stone thrown horizontally, follow parabolic pathways.

+

$+q$

uniform electric field

−

For a charged body moving in a magnetic field, the force is inevitably perpendicular to the velocity. So it acts as a centripetal force and the result is circular motion.

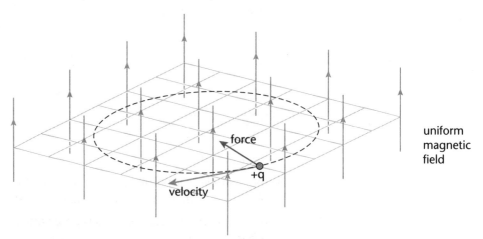

uniform magnetic field

For a charged body moving in an electric field and a magnetic field that are at right angles to each other, the forces can be in opposite directions. They can balance, resulting in no deflection of the charged body's pathway. This happens when:

Eq = Bqv

v = E/B

So, by adjusting the values of the field strengths, E and B, it is possible to select charged bodies of a particular velocity to travel in a straight line.

uniform electric field and uniform magnetic field, here producing equal and opposite forces on charges of a particular velocity

Progress check

1 The Moon orbits the Earth, mass 6.0×10^{24} kg, at a radius of 3.84×10^8 m.
   $G = 6.7 \times 10^{-11}$ N m^2 kg^{-2}.
   Calculate:
   a   the speed of the Moon in its orbit.
   b   the time it takes for the Moon to complete one orbit.

2 An electron of mass $m_e = 9.10 \times 10^{-31}$ kg and charge, $e = 1.60 \times 10^{-19}$ C travels at a speed of 2.10×10^7 m s^{-1} in a circular orbit at right angles to a magnetic field.
   The magnetic field strength, $B = 6.5 \times 10^{-6}$ T.
   Calculate the radius of the electron orbit.

3 In the diagram of the cyclotron what is the direction of the magnetic field?

3 Upwards.

2 18.4 m

b 2.36×10^6 s
1 a 1.02×10^3 m s^{-1}

2.6 Electromagnetic induction

After studying this section you should be able to:

- *calculate the flux linkage through a coil of wire in a magnetic field*
- *explain how electromagnetic induction occurs due to changes in flux linkage*
- *apply Faraday's law and Lenz's law*

LEARNING SUMMARY

Flux and flux linkage

AQA A	4	Edexcel context	4
AQA B	4	OCR A	option
CCEA	A2.2	OCR B	G495
Edexcel concept	4	WJEC	5

Flux provides a useful model for explaining the effects of magnetic fields.

The current view is that these forces can be attributed to 'exchange particles'.

Electromagnetic induction is used to generate electricity in power stations and to transform its voltage as it passes through the distribution system.

The effects of induction can be explained by using the concept of **flux**. Although the actual existence of flux has long been discredited, it still provides a useful modelling tool and an awareness of its meaning is useful to understand the laws of induction as set out by Faraday and Lenz.

Like gravitational and electric fields, magnetic fields act at a distance. Magnetic field patterns are used to show the forces that are exerted around a magnet or electric current. These forces are exerted without any physical contact between the magnet or current that causes the field and a magnetic material or current placed within the field. In the days of Faraday and Lenz, they were explained in terms of flux.

When drawing magnetic field patterns:

- the relative strength at different points in the field is shown by the separation of the field lines
- the closer the lines are together, the stronger the field
- these field lines represent **magnetic flux**, which is imagined as occupying the space around a magnet and being responsible for the effect of a magnet field.

To integrate the flux model with today's explanation of magnetic effects in terms of magnetic field strength, this can be thought of in terms of a flux density, being represented by the concentration of magnetic field lines. Flux density is the flux per unit area so flux is now defined in terms of the magnetic field strength and the area that the field permeates.

This definition relates the equivalence of the modern concept of magnetic field strength to that of the older 'flux density' concept.

> The magnetic flux, ϕ, through an area, A, is defined as the product of the magnetic field strength and the area normal to the field.
>
> $$\phi = B \times A$$
>
> Magnetic flux is measured in webers (Wb) where 1 Wb is the flux through an area of 1 m² normal to a uniform field of strength 1 T.
>
> **KEY POINT**

The diagram shows the flux through a rectangular coil in a uniform magnetic field.

coil of N turns and area A

magnetic field of strength B, and flux ϕ

The flux through a rectangular coil

Movement of the coil parallel to the field does not induce an e.m.f., since no field lines are being 'cut'.

The induced e.m.f. has its greatest value when the movement of the coil is perpendicular to the field.

When the coil is rotated, it 'cuts' through the flux, or field lines and an e.m.f. is induced.

The size, or magnitude, of the induced e.m.f. depends on:

• the amount of flux through the coil
• the speed of rotation
• the number of turns on the coil.

Each turn on the coil has a **flux linkage** which changes as the coil rotates.

The flux linkage of a coil of N turns is $N\phi$, where ϕ is the flux through the coil.

Faraday's law

AQA A	4	Edexcel context	4
AQA B	4	OCR A	G485
CCEA	A2.2	OCR B	G495
Edexcel concept	4	WJEC	5

In a power station, electricity is generated by an electromagnet spinning inside copper coils.

Electromagnetic induction occurs whenever the magnetic field through a conductor changes. This can be due to a conductor moving through a magnetic field or a conductor being in a fixed position within a changing magnetic field, such as that due to an alternating current. Both of these result in an e.m.f. being induced in the conductor.

Examples of electromagnetic induction include:

• moving a magnet inside a wire coil
• generating the high voltage necessary to a) ionise the vapour in a fluorescent tube or b) cause the spark needed to ignite the explosive mixture in a petrol engine
• changing the voltage of an alternating current, using a transformer.

The diagram below shows the difference in the size of the e.m.f. when a magnet is moved at different speeds in a coil.

slow movement
produces a small e.m.f.

faster movement
produces a bigger e.m.f.

Faraday's law relates the size of the induced e.m.f. to the change in flux linkage.

To generate the high voltage needed to cause a spark, the flux has to change rapidly. This happens when the current in an electromagnet is switched off.

> Faraday's law states that:
>
> *the size of the induced e.m.f. is proportional to the rate of change of flux linkage.*
>
> As the proportionality constant is equal to 1, for a uniform rate of change of flux linkage this can be written as:
>
> $$\text{magnitude of induced e.m.f.} = N\,\frac{\Delta\phi}{\Delta t}$$
>
> where $\Delta\phi$ is the change of flux in time Δt.

KEY POINT

What direction?

AQA A	4	Edexcel context	4
AQA B	4	OCR A	G485
CCEA	A2.2	OCR B	G495
Edexcel concept	4	WJEC	5

Faraday's law can be used to work out the size of an induced e.m.f. such as that across the wingtips of an aircraft flying in the Earth's magnetic field. In Britain the Earth's field makes an angle of about 20° with the vertical, see the following diagram.

20°

Unlike that of a bar magnet, the Earth's magnetic field is from South to North. It can be considered to have two components, vertical and horizontal.

An aircraft flying in a North–South direction is cutting across the vertical component only, while flying East–West involves cutting across the horizontal component in addition.

The induced e.m.f. arises as a consequence of the force on the free electrons in the metal of the aircraft frame. Fleming's left hand rule can be used to work out the direction of the force on the electrons and hence the direction of the induced e.m.f.

All the charged particles experience a force due to their movement through a magnetic field, but the force is too weak to affect anything other than the free electrons.

In the case of an aircraft flying from North to South:

- the current is South–North (since electron travel is North–South)
- the magnetic field being 'cut' is vertically downwards
- the force on the free electrons is towards the West.

This results in a charge imbalance and a voltage, or e.m.f., across the wingtips.

The direction of the e.m.f. induced in the aircraft and when a magnet moves into a coil of wire can be worked out using **Lenz's law**.

In the case of the aircraft the change producing the e.m.f. is the aircraft's motion. If the induced e.m.f. in the aircraft caused electrons to slow continuously from East to West, it would produce a force in a Northerly direction – opposite to the motion of the aircraft.

This does not happen, however, because there is no complete circuit.

> **KEY POINT**
>
> Lenz's law states that:
>
> *the direction of an induced e.m.f. is always in opposition to the change that causes it.*

The diagram below shows that when the North pole of a magnet is moved into one end of a coil, the induced e.m.f. causes an induced current in an anticlockwise direction. When current passes in a coil, the magnetic field is similar to that of a bar magnet, the North pole being the end where the current passes anticlockwise.

The direction of the current is always such as to repel the approaching magnet – *the induced e.m.f. opposes the change that produces it.*

The direction of the induced current is reversed by reversing the magnet or its direction of movement.

The induced current when a magnet enters a coil of wire

direction of current

How to identify the poles of an electromagnet

If the induced current was in the opposite direction, it would attract the magnet into the coil and generate electricity with no energy input.

Lenz's law is a re-statement of the principle of conservation of energy; the induced current opposes the motion of the magnet so work has to be done to move the magnet against the induced magnetic field. This work is the energy transfer to the circuit needed to cause a current.

Combining Faraday's and Lenz's laws gives the equation for induced e.m.f.:

> **KEY POINT**
>
> $$\varepsilon = -N\frac{\Delta\phi}{\Delta t}$$
>
> Where ε is the induced e.m.f. The negative sign shows that the induced e.m.f. is in opposition to the change of flux causing it.

The transformer

Transformers use changing magnetic fields to change the size of an alternating voltage. An alternating current passing in one coil (the primary) induces an e.m.f. in an adjacent coil (the secondary).

The diagram below shows the flux when the two coils are wound on an iron core.

Flux linking two transformer coils

> The *e.m.f.* is induced whether or not there is a secondary circuit. If there is a complete circuit, there is also an induced *current*.

In a transformer:

- alternating current in the primary produces an alternating magnetic field
- this is reinforced by the high-permeability iron core
- the flux concentrates in the iron
- an e.m.f. is induced in the secondary because of the changing flux linkage.

> Iron is easily magnetised; its magnetic domains contribute to the strength of the magnetic field.

It follows from the last bullet point that the induced e.m.f. is proportional to the number of turns on the secondary coil.

> A transformer constructed from low-resistance coils on a laminated iron core is close to ideal.

KEY POINT

The relationship between the voltages and numbers of turns for an ideal transformer is:

$$\frac{V_p}{V_s} = \frac{N_p}{N_s}$$

This states that the voltages are in the same ratio as the numbers of turns. In an ideal transformer there is no energy loss in the wires or the core so the power output from the secondary is equal to the power input to the primary and the currents are in the inverse ratio to the voltages. (In reality, energy dissipation is significant.)

High voltage transmission

In transmission of power from a 'supply' or power station to users or 'load' (made up of lots of hair-driers, TV sets, industrial power tools, and so on) this is an ideal situation:

In this ideal situation, power in = power out = IV

Note that power can be large even if current, I or voltage, V, are small, provided that the other is large enough to compensate.

In reality, despite the thickness of the cables used, they have some resistance which means that they transfer energy to their surroundings by heating. Thus power intended for the user is lost, at economic and environmental expense. The fact that the cables are very many kilometres long worsens the problem.

Now, power in = power available for load + power loss from cables.

It is important to reduce the power loss from cables as much as possible. This loss can be calculated from:

power loss from cables = I²R, where R is the cable resistance.

Clearly the power loss is very dependent on current. So power should be transmitted using low current in the long transmission cables. Fortunately, this can be achieved, using transformers to 'step' the voltage up to high values and then down again for consumers.

Progress check

1. A rectangular coil has 25 turns and an area of 2.5×10^{-4} m².
   It is placed in a magnetic field of strength 6.8×10^{-6} T.
   Calculate the flux linkage when the plane of the coil is
   a parallel to the magnetic field
   b perpendicular to the magnetic field.

2. An aircraft flies from East to West.
   In what direction is the induced e.m.f. due to the 'cutting' of the Earth's horizontal magnetic field?

3. The flux linking a coil of 60 turns changes at the rate of 4.0×10^{-3} Wb s⁻¹.
   Calculate the size of the induced e.m.f.

3 0.24 V

2 The top of the aircraft is positive and the bottom negative

1 a 0
  b 4.25×10^{-8} Wb

Sample question and model answer

The diagram shows a capacitor connected in series with a 12.0 V power supply and a 500 Ω resistor.

The switch is closed.

(a) When the switch is first closed, what is the initial voltage across:
  (i)   the capacitor?   [1]

At the instant that the switch is closed there is no charge on the capacitor, so there is no voltage across it. All the voltage is therefore across the resistor.

  0 V   1 mark

  (ii) the resistor?   [1]

  12 V   1 mark

(b) Calculate the value of the current in the circuit immediately after the switch is closed.   [3]

The value of the resistor determines the initial current in the circuit.

  I = V ÷ R   1 mark
    = 12.0 V ÷ 500 Ω   1 mark
    = 0.024 A   1 mark

(c) When the capacitor is fully charged, calculate:
  (i)   the charge stored on the capacitor   [3]

  Q = C x V   1 mark
    = 200 μF x 12.0 V   1 mark
    = 2.4 x 10⁻³ C   1 mark

  (ii) the energy stored by the capacitor.   [3]

Alternatively, $\frac{1}{2}QV$ should give the same answer, provided that the charge, Q, has been calculated correctly.

  $E = \frac{1}{2} C \times V^2$ 1 mark

    $= \frac{1}{2} \times 200 \, μF \times 12.0^2$ 1 mark

    $= 1.44 \times 10^{-2}$ J   1 mark

(d) The capacitor is discharged and a second 200 μF capacitor is connected in parallel with the capacitor shown in the diagram. The switch is then closed. Without doing any further calculations, explain how this affects:
  (i)   the final charge stored   [2]

As the question states that further calculations are not required, give an answer based on the relationships used to calculate these quantities, with the reasons.

  This is doubled (1 mark) since the potential difference is unchanged and the capacitance is doubled (1 mark).

  (ii) the final energy stored.   [2]

  This is also doubled (1 mark) as there is double the capacitance (and double the amount of charge stored) for the same potential difference (1 mark).

Practice examination questions

Throughout this section, use the following values of constants:

electronic charge, $e = -1.6 \times 10^{-19}$ C

universal gravitational constant, $G = 6.7 \times 10^{-11}$ Nm² kg⁻²

$k = 1/4\pi\varepsilon_0 = 9.0 \times 10^9$ Nm² C⁻²

gravitational field strength at the surface of the Earth, $g = 10.0$ N kg⁻¹

1

A hydrogen atom consists of a proton and an electron at an average separation of 5.2×10^{-11} m.

(a) Calculate the size of the force between them. [3]

(b) (i) Calculate the electric field strength that each experiences due to the other. [3]

   (ii) What is the direction of the electric field between the proton and the electron? [1]

(c) Assuming that the electron orbits the proton, calculate the speed of its orbit. The mass of an electron, $m_e = 9.1 \times 10^{-31}$ kg. [3]

2

The diagram shows a pair of parallel plates connected to 2500 V supply.

An oil drop of mass 0.050 g between the plates carries a charge of 10e.

(a) Calculate:

   (i) the voltage between C and D [1]

   (ii) the energy transfer when the drop moves from C to D. [3]

(b) Calculate the energy transfer when the drop moves from A to B. [1]

(c) The voltage is changed so that the drop is stationary between the plates.

   (i) What must the polarity of the plates be to achieve this? [1]

   (ii) Calculate the voltage required. [3]

3

Use this data to answer the questions:

The mass of the Earth = 6.0×10^{24} kg.

The mass of the Moon = 7.4×10^{21} kg.

The distance between the Earth and the Moon = 3.8×10^8 m.

(a) (i) Calculate the strength of the Earth's gravitational field at the Moon's orbit. [3]

   (ii) Calculate the size of the Earth's pull on the Moon. [2]

   (iii) Use the answer to (ii) to calculate the Moon's period of rotation around the Earth. [3]

(b) Tides are due to the combined effect of the Moon and the Sun.

(i) Calculate the size of the Moon's pull on 1.0 kg of water. [3]

(ii) Suggest why the pull of the Sun has much less effect than the pull of the Moon on tides. [3]

(iii) The diagram shows two positions of the Moon relative to the Earth and the Sun.

Suggest why tides are higher when the Moon is in position A than when it is in position B. [2]

4

A moving coil loudspeaker consists of a cylindrical permanent magnet and an electromagnet. The electromagnet is positioned between the poles of the fixed magnet. The diagram shows the arrangement.

(a) What is the direction of the magnetic field between the poles of the fixed magnet? [1]

(b) The current in the electromagnet passes in a clockwise direction. What is the direction of the force on the electromagnet? [1]

(c) Explain why the electromagnet vibrates when an alternating current passes in it. [2]

(d) The value of the magnetic field strength due to the fixed magnet is 0.85 T at the position of the electromagnet. The electromagnet consists of a coil of wire of 150 turns and diameter 5.0 cm. Calculate the size of the force on the coil when a current of 0.055 A passes in it. [3]

5

Electrons can be made to move in a circular path by firing them into a region where there is a magnetic field acting at right angles to their velocity.

The diagram shows a device for producing high-speed electrons.

(a) Calculate:

    (i) the kinetic energy of an electron in the accelerated beam   [3]

    (ii) the speed of an electron in the accelerated beam.
        The mass of an electron, $m_e = 9.1 \times 10^{-31}$ kg.   [3]

(b) The electron beam passes into a magnetic field directed into the paper.

    (i) What is the direction of the force on the electron beam as it enters the magnetic field?   [1]

    (ii) Explain why the electrons follow a circular path.   [2]

    (iii) The strength of the magnetic field is 2.0 mT.
        Calculate the radius of the circular path of the electrons.   [2]

6

A rectangular coil of wire is placed so that its plane is perpendicular to a magnetic field of strength 0.15 T. This is shown in the diagram.

(a) Calculate the magnetic flux through the coil:

    (i) when the coil is in the position shown in the diagram   [3]

    (ii) when the coil is turned through 90°.   [1]

(b) The coil is connected to a high-resistance voltmeter.

    (i) Describe and explain how the reading on the voltmeter changes as the coil is rotated through 360°.   [4]

    (ii) What device makes use of this effect?   [1]

(c) State three ways of increasing the size of the induced voltage.   [3]

Chapter 3

Thermal and particle physics

The following topics are covered in this chapter:

- *A model gas*
- *Internal energy*
- *Radioactive decay*
- *Energy from the nucleus*

- *Probing matter*
- *Accelerators and detectors*
- *Quantum phenomena*

3.1 A model gas

After studying this section you should be able to:

- *understand the concept of absolute zero of temperature and be able to convert temperatures between the Celsius and Kelvin scales*
- *recall and use the ideal gas equation of state $pV = nRT$*
- *explain the relationship between the kelvin temperature and the mean kinetic energy of the particles of an ideal gas*

LEARNING SUMMARY

Gas pressure

AQA A	5	Edexcel context	5
AQA B	4	OCR A	G484
CCEA	A2.1	OCR B	G494
Edexcel concept	5	WJEC	4

As you will see later in this section, the average speed of the particles is different for different gases at the same temperature.

Brownian motion was first observed by Robert Brown while studying pollen grains suspended in water. The explanation of Brownian motion is due to Einstein.

The kinetic model pictures a gas as being made up of large numbers of individual particles in constant motion. At normal pressures and temperatures the particles are widely-spaced compared to their size. The motion of an individual particle is:

- **rapid** – a typical average speed at room temperature is 500 m s^{-1}
- **random** in both speed and direction – these are constantly changing due to the effects of collisions.

Gases exert **pressure** on the walls of their container and any other objects that they are in contact with. This pressure acts in all directions and is due to the forces as particles collide and rebound.

Evidence for this movement of gas particles comes from **Brownian motion**; the random, lurching movement of comparatively massive particles such as smoke specks when suspended in air. This movement is attributed to the bombardment by much smaller air particles which are too small to be seen by an optical microscope and must therefore be moving very rapidly.

Gas particles are widely spaced. Their movement is random in both speed and direction.

Experiments show that increasing the temperature of a gas also increases the pressure that it exerts. At higher temperatures the average speed of the particles increases. This affects the pressure in two ways:

- it increases the average force of the collisions
- collisions are more frequent.

The graph shows how the pressure of a gas depends on its Celsius temperature when the volume is kept constant. Although the graph is a straight line, it does not show that pressure is directly proportional to Celsius temperature since the line does not go through the origin.

This is not surprising since 0°C does not represent 'no temperature'; it is merely a reference point that is convenient to use because it is easily reproduced.

The graph does however give an indication of whereabouts 'no temperature' is on the Celsius scale. The temperature of a body determines whether it will exchange energy with its surroundings. Remember that energy transfers between bodies at different temperatures, and the net (overall) flow is from the hotter to the cooler. So the lowest possible temperature is that at which a body can only *receive* energy from the surroundings. It then has no internal energy and its particles have no motion. By extrapolating the graph back to the corresponding pressure, zero, it gives a figure for the minimum temperature at –273°C.

> The extrapolation assumes that the substance remains a gas as it is cooled. Real gases would reach their boiling point and liquefy before the minimum temperature was reached.

Knowledge of the zero of temperature allows it to be measured on an absolute scale. On an absolute scale of measurement the zero is the minimum amount of a quantity – it is not possible for a smaller measurement to exist.

> Note that the kelvin is not called a degree and does not have a ° in the unit.

KEY POINT

The absolute scale of temperature is called the Kelvin scale; its unit is the kelvin (K) and its relationship to the Celsius scale, to the nearest whole number, is:

$$T/K = \theta/°C + 273$$

The diagram shows the relationship between Celsius and kelvin temperatures.

> Since there is no such thing as perfect insulation a body can never be at absolute zero. There would always be energy flow to the body.

> The value of the constant depends on the amount of gas (measured in moles) and its volume.

> Remember: the relationship is only valid when temperature is measured in kelvin.

When Celsius temperatures are converted to kelvins, the experimental results show that:

KEY POINT

For a fixed mass of gas at constant volume:

$$\text{pressure} \propto \text{absolute temperature}$$

or:

$$p/T = \text{constant}$$

The ideal gas equation

AQA A	5	Edexcel context	5
AQA B	4	OCR A	G484
CCEA	A2.1	OCR B	G494
Edexcel concept	5	WJEC	4

When experimenting with a fixed mass of gas the three variables are pressure, volume and temperature. Fixing one of these enables the relationship between the other two to be established. In addition to the relationship between pressure and temperature above:

> The relationship $pV =$ constant is known as Boyle's law.

KEY POINT

For a fixed mass of gas at constant temperature, pressure is inversely proportional to volume:

$$\text{pressure} \propto 1/\text{volume} \quad \text{or } pV = \text{constant}$$

For a fixed mass of gas at constant pressure, the volume is proportional to absolute temperature:

$$\text{volume} \propto \text{temperature} \quad \text{or } V/T = \text{constant}$$

Halving the volume of a gas leads to twice the rate of collisions – doubling the pressure. This is an example of Boyle's Law.

These relationships are based on experiments. They are valid for all real gases to a high level of precision provided that the gas is neither at a high pressure nor close to its boiling point. They lead to the concept of an **ideal gas** as one that obeys Boyle's law in all conditions, i.e. a gas for which pV = constant.

> The concept of an ideal gas is useful because the behaviour of all gases is close to ideal provided that certain conditions about temperature and pressure are met.

Real gases do not obey Boyle's law when the particles are close enough together so that they occupy a significant proportion of the gas's volume and exert appreciable forces on each other.

For an ideal gas the three gas laws can be combined into the single equation:

$$pV/T = \text{constant}$$

In this case the value of the constant depends only on the amount of gas. For 1 mole of any gas under ideal conditions it has the value of 8.3 J mol^{-1} K^{-1}. This constant is called the **molar gas constant** and has the symbol R. Doubling the number of particles by considering two moles of gas has the same effect as doubling the value of the constant, so:

> 1 mole of gas consists of the Avogadro constant, N_{AV} of particles. The value of the Avogadro constant is 6.02×10^{23} mol^{-1}.

The equation of state for an ideal gas is: $$pV = nRT$$ where n is the number of moles of gas and R is the molar gas constant.	**KEY POINT**

An algebraic model

If a gas is sealed in a container, then increasing its temperature results in an increase in the pressure of the gas. This can be attributed to an increase in the average speed of the particles. The kinetic model can be extended to establish the relationship between the temperature of a gas and the speed of the particles. First of all it is necessary to establish just what is meant by 'ideal gas behaviour'.

The kinetic theory of gases involves some basic assumptions about the particles of a gas:

- a gas consists of a large number of particles in a state of rapid, random motion
- gas pressure is a result of collisions between the particles and the container walls.

In addition, for an ideal gas it is assumed that:

- the volume occupied by the particles is negligible
- intermolecular forces are negligible
- all collisions are elastic, so there is no loss in kinetic energy.

> Note that working out $<c^2>$ involves:
> - listing all the individual particle speeds
> - squaring them
> - calculating the mean of the squares.
>
> $$<c^2> = \frac{C_1^2 + C_2^2 + C_3^2 + \dots C_n^2}{n}$$

With these assumptions, it can be shown that the pressure of an enclosed sample of an ideal gas is proportional to the mean of the squares of the particle speeds:

$$pV = \tfrac{1}{3} Nm <c^2>$$ Where N = total number of particles m = mass of each particle $<c^2>$ = mean of the squares of the particle speeds	**KEY POINT**

Alternatively, since Nm/V = mass ÷ volume = density:

$$p = \frac{1}{3}\rho <c^2>$$

Where ρ = density of the gas

If the mass and volume of an ideal gas are fixed, the gas pressure is proportional to its temperature, p/T = constant. The above results show that, as pressure is proportional to $<c^2>$ it must be proportional to the mean kinetic energy of the particles.

These factors taken together give the relationship between kinetic energy and temperature:

the mean kinetic energy of the particles of an ideal gas is proportional to the kelvin temperature

$$\frac{1}{2}m<c^2> \propto T$$

K E Y P O I N T

This means that doubling the kelvin temperature of a gas doubles the mean kinetic energy and the mean square speed of its particles. Remember that these relationships apply to all ideal gases, irrespective of the gas. So at a particular temperature the mean kinetic energy of the molecules in a sample of hydrogen is the same as those in a sample of oxygen. Since an oxygen molecule has sixteen times the mass of a hydrogen molecule, the mean square speed of the hydrogen molecules must be sixteen times as great as that of oxygen molecules.

The Boltzmann constant

AQA A	5	Edexcel context	5
AQA B	4	OCR A	G484
CCEA	A2.1	OCR B	G494
Edexcel concept	5	WJEC	4

The algebraic model can be used to put a figure on the mean kinetic energy of the particles of an ideal gas at any temperature.

For one mole of gas the number of particles, N, is equal to Avogadro's number, N_A. So for one mole, combining the equations pV = RT and $pV = \frac{1}{3}N_A m<c^2>$ gives:

$$\frac{1}{2}m<c^2> = \frac{3}{2}RT/N_A \text{ or } N_A \times \frac{1}{2}m<c^2> = \frac{3}{2}RT$$

This means that the total kinetic energy of one mole of an ideal gas is equal to $\frac{3}{2}RT$, since N_A is the number of particles and $\frac{1}{2}m<c^2>$ is their mean kinetic energy.

The Boltzmann constant, k, relates the mean kinetic energy of the particles in an ideal gas directly to temperature:

$$\frac{1}{2}m<c^2> = \frac{3}{2}RT/N_A$$
$$= \frac{3}{2}kT$$

Where $k = R/N_A$ is the Boltzmann constant and has the value 1.38×10^{-23} J K^{-1}

K E Y P O I N T

To work out the mass of a molecule of a gas, divide the molar mass by the Avogadro constant.

So, for example, at a temperature of 20°C (293 K) the mean kinetic energy of the particles of an ideal gas is equal to $\frac{3}{2} \times 1.38 \times 10^{-23}$ J K^{-1} $\times$ 293 K = 6.07×10^{-21} J. This may seem a tiny amount of energy, but remember that it refers to a single gas particle which has a very small mass.

Progress check

Assume that R = 8.3 J mol⁻¹ K⁻¹

1 Calculate the molar volume of an ideal gas at atmospheric pressure (1.01 × 10⁵ Pa) and a temperature of 0°C.

2 The mean kinetic energy of the particles of an ideal gas is 6.07 × 10⁻²¹ J at a temperature of 20°C. At what temperature is their mean kinetic energy equal to 12.14 × 10⁻²¹ J?

3 2.0 mol of an ideal gas is sealed in a container of volume 5.5 × 10⁻² m³.
a Calculate the pressure of the gas at a temperature of 18°C.
b At what Celsius temperature would the pressure of the gas be doubled?

4 1.0 mol of oxygen has a mass of 32 g. Calculate the mean square speed of the molecules at 0°C and a pressure of 1.01 × 10⁵ Pa.

5 A room measures 3.5 m × 3.2 m × 2.2 m. It contains gas at a pressure of 1.03 × 10⁵ Pa and a temperature of 25°C. Calculate the number of moles of gas in the room.

1 2.24×10^{-2} m³
2 586 K or 313°C
3 a 8.8×10^4 Pa
b 309°C
4 2.1×10^5 m² s⁻²
5 1026

3.2 Internal energy

After studying this section you should be able to:

- *explain the meaning of* specific heat capacity *and* specific latent heat *and use the appropriate relationships*
- *describe the principle of operation of a* heat engine *and a* heat pump
- *calculate the maximum efficiency of a heat engine*

LEARNING SUMMARY

Energy of individual particles

AQA A	5	Edexcel context	5
AQA B	5	OCR A	G484
CCEA	A2.1	OCR B	G494
Edexcel concept	5	WJEC	4

All materials are made up of particles, and particles have energy. The particles of an ideal gas have only kinetic energy since forces between the particles are negligible. However, this is not true of a solid or a liquid, and the particles in real gases exert some force on each other whenever they are close enough together and especially during collisions.

Imagine a collision between two particles in a real gas:

> The speed of colliding particles is momentarily zero as their direction of travel is reversed.

- as the particles approach, the attractive forces cause an increase in the speed and kinetic energy
- the particles then get closer, the force between them becomes repulsive and the speed decreases, being momentarily zero before they start to separate
- the process is then reversed.

There is an interchange between potential (stored) energy and kinetic energy during the collision, as shown in the diagram.

> As the separation between two particles decreases, the net force changes from attractive to repulsive. The equilibrium position is where these forces are equal in size, so the resultant force is zero.

particles speed up due to short-range attractive forces

particles slow down due to close-range repulsive forces

The particles of real gases, like those of solids and liquids, have both potential and kinetic energy. The distribution of energy between kinetic and potential is constantly changing and so is said to be random.

The total amount of energy of the particles in an object is known as its **internal energy**. At a constant temperature the internal energy of an object remains unchanged, but the contributions of individual particles to that energy change due to the transfer of energy during interactions between particles.

Being specific

AQA A	5	Edexcel context	5
AQA B	5	OCR A	G484
CCEA	A2.1	OCR B	G494
Edexcel concept	5	WJEC	4

Changing the temperature of an object involves a change in its internal energy, the total potential and kinetic energy of the particles. One way of doing this is to place the object in thermal contact with a hotter or colder object, so that there is a net flow of energy from hot to cold (see diagram).

> Two objects are in thermal contact if they can exchange heat. Energy flows both ways between a warm and a cold object in thermal contact, but there is more energy flow from the warm object to the cold one than the other way.

a cold dish in a hot oven

warm food placed in a refrigerator

The energy flow between objects at different temperatures

The energy transfer required to change the temperature of an object depends on:

- the temperature change
- the mass of the object
- the material the object is made from.

These are all taken into consideration in the concept of **specific heat capacity**. The term 'specific' means 'for each kilogram', so any physical measurement that is described as 'specific' refers to 'per kilogram of material'.

> When using this relationship the temperatures can be in either Celsius or kelvin since the temperature change is the same in each case.

KEY POINT

The specific heat capacity of a material, c, is defined as:
The energy transfer required to change the temperature of 1 kg of the material by 1°C.

$$\Delta E = mc\,\Delta\theta$$

where c, specific heat capacity, is measured in J kg^{-1} °C^{-1} or J kg^{-1} K^{-1}

Changing phase

AQA A	5	Edexcel context	5
AQA B	5	OCR A	G484
CCEA	A2.1	OCR B	G494
Edexcel concept	5	WJEC	4

If you try to squash a solid or a liquid, the particles are pushed closer together and they repel each other. Stretching has the opposite effect; when the separation of the particles is increased the forces are attractive. At increased separations the particles have increased potential energy and this energy has to be supplied for any process that involves expansion to take place.

> The term 'phase' means whether the substance is a solid, liquid or gas.

When a substance changes **phase** there is a change in the potential energy of the particles. For most substances there is a small increase in potential energy when changing from solid to liquid and a much bigger change from liquid to gas.

> The increase in particle separation during a change of phase from solid to liquid is small, but that during a change of phase from liquid to gas is large.

solid   liquid   gas

There is a small increase in potential energy of the particles when a substance changes from solid to liquid, and a much larger increase in changing from liquid to gas.

The energy absorbed or released during a change of phase is called **latent heat**. As with heat capacity, the term 'specific latent heat' refers to 1 kilogram of material.

> This definition applies to a change of phase where energy is removed from the substance, as well as a change where energy is supplied.

KEY POINT

The specific latent heat of a material, l, is defined as:
The energy required to change the phase of 1 kg of the material without changing its temperature.

$$E = ml$$

Note that there are two values of the specific latent heat for any material:

- the specific latent heat of fusion refers to a change of phase between solid and liquid
- the specific latent heat of vaporisation refers to a change of phase between liquid and gas.

On each horizontal part of the curve the substance exists in two phases. Can you identify them?

The diagram shows a typical temperature–time graph as a solid is heated at a constant rate and passes through the three phases. Where the curve is horizontal it shows that energy is being absorbed with no change in temperature. This corresponds to a change of phase. Note that much more energy is absorbed during the change from liquid to gas than during the change from solid to liquid.

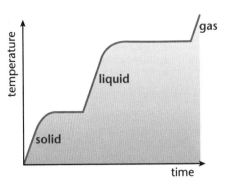

Heat and work

AQA A   5   WJEC   4
AQA B   5

Placing an object in thermal contact with one that is hotter or colder, for example an immersion heater or the inside of a freezer, is one way of changing its temperature. It is a simple thermal process. Anyone who has ever pumped up a bicycle tyre is aware that compressing the air in the pump also causes it to become warmer. A person using a pump does work on the air. This could be called a mechanical process.

Compressing a gas causes heating and expanding a gas causes cooling. Whether the gas is heated or cooled depends on whether work is done **on** it or **by** it.

Other everyday examples of work causing a change in temperature include:

- striking a match, where work done against friction forces results in heating of the match head
- release of a pressurised gas, where the rapid expansion of the gas does work to push surrounding air out of the way; this requires energy transfer and causes cooling.

The **first law of thermodynamics** states the internal energy of a gas depends only on its state, i.e. the conditions of temperature, pressure and volume and the amount of gas, and not how it reached that state. Transferring energy as heat to a gas has the same effect as doing work on it – they both cause an increase in the internal energy, and therefore the temperature.

In other words, the first law states that working and heating are equivalent.

Q is the energy transferred to the gas by thermal processes.

W is the energy transferred to the gas by mechanical processes.

The first law of thermodynamics can be written as:

increase in internal energy of gas = $\dfrac{\text{heat transferred}}{\text{to gas}}$ + $\dfrac{\text{work done}}{\text{on gas}}$

$$\Delta U = Q + W$$

Note that the values of ΔU, Q and W are negative if the internal energy decreases or heat is removed from the gas or work is done by the gas.

KEY POINT

Heat engines

AQA A   5
AQA B   5

In internal combustion engines:

- the burning of fuel supplies heat to a gas, increasing its internal energy
- the gas does work as it pushes the pistons, decreasing the internal energy.

Energy that is not removed from the gases by pushing the pistons is wasted in the exhaust gases and passes to the atmosphere, which is at a lower temperature.

Rockets, jet engines and steam engines are all examples of heat engines.

This illustrates what is meant by a **heat engine**; a device that uses the energy flow from a **hot source** to a **cold sink** to do work. The principle of operation of a heat engine is shown in the diagram.

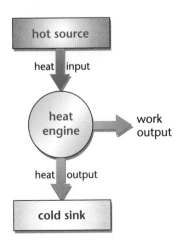

91

It is not possible to extract all the internal energy from the steam in a steam turbine. Can you explain why?

The steam turbines that drive the generators in power stations are also heat engines. Steam enters the turbines at high temperature and pressure and leaves at much lower temperature and pressure. Of the internal energy lost by the steam:

• some does work on the turbines
• some is lost to the surroundings.

The turbines are designed to extract as much energy from the steam as possible; the greater the proportion of the available energy extracted, the more efficient the process is.

If there are no energy losses, then the maximum efficiency of a heat engine is given by the relationship:

> **KEY POINT**
>
> maximum efficiency = $(T_H - T_c) \div T_H$
> where T_H is the temperature of the hot source and T_c is the temperature of the cold sink. Both temperatures are measured in kelvin.

Efficiency is defined as:
useful energy output
—————————————
total energy input

It is usually expressed as a fraction or decimal, which can be multiplied by 100 to give a percentage efficiency.

For example, if steam enters a turbine at 250°C (523 K) and leaves at 120°C (393 K) then the maximum efficiency is (523 K – 393 K) ÷ 523 K = 0.25. In practice, real heat engines do not operate at their maximum efficiency since there are always other energy losses.

Heat pumps

AQA A 5
AQA B 5

When two objects at different temperatures are placed in simple thermal contact, the net energy flow is from hot to cold. No other energy source is needed to drive this flow, although sometimes fans are used to speed up the natural process. In refrigeration, the direction of energy flow is from cold to hot. To achieve this, an external source of energy is needed to drive a **heat pump**.

Some ovens and convector heaters use fans to speed up the rate of energy transfer.

The principle of a refrigerator is shown in the diagram.

The pipes at the back of a refrigerator are painted black. How does this help to remove energy?

A volatile liquid is one that evaporates easily.

• Volatile liquid evaporates as it is forced through a narrow jet inside the refrigerator.
• This evaporation causes cooling and the cold vapour absorbs energy from its surroundings.
• The vapour returns to the compressor unit where it is compressed, causing it to become heated.
• Energy is dissipated to the surroundings as the hot vapour passes through pipes outside the fridge, where it condenses.

This method of heating a building can be used effectively where there is a convenient river to extract the energy from.

Heat pumps are also used to heat buildings by extracting energy from the surroundings. The energy available for heating is more than the energy needed to drive the pump, so this method is both cost-efficient and energy-efficient.

Entropy

Entropy is a measure of the disorder of a system.

In an isolated system, entropy increases over time. For example, particles of two gases that are neatly separated into two spaces will mix together to create a disordered mixture.

For non-isolated systems, it is possible for entropy to decrease, but this requires an input of energy.

Progress check

1 1.5 kg water at 10°C is placed in a kettle. Calculate the energy transferred to the water in bringing it to the boil. The specific heat capacity of water, $c = 4.2 \times 10^3$ J kg^{-1} °C^{-1}.

2 Hot water enters a central heating radiator at a temperature of 52°C and leaves it at a temperature of 39°C. The specific heat capacity of water is 4200 J kg^{-1} K^{-1}.
   a Calculate the energy transfer from each kg of water that passes through the radiator.
   b If the rate of flow of water through the radiator is 3.0 kg min^{-1}, calculate the power output of the radiator.

3 The specific latent heat of vaporization of nitrogen is 2.0×10^5 J kg^{-1}. Calculate the energy required to change 0.65 kg of liquid nitrogen into vapour without changing its temperature.

4 Some air is trapped in a sealed syringe. The piston is pushed in and does 450 J of work on the air. While this is happening 300 J of heat flows out of the air.
   a Calculate the change in internal energy of the air.
   b Explain whether the air ends up hotter or colder than it was to start with.

4 a +150 J   b hotter as the internal energy has increased.
3 1.30 × 10⁵ J
2 a 5.46 × 10⁴ J   b 2.73 kW
1 5.67 × 10⁵ J

3.3 Radioactive decay

Radiation all around us

AQA A	5	Edexcel context	5
AQA B	5	OCR A	G485
CCEA	A2.1	OCR B	G494
Edexcel concept	5	WJEC	5

The term 'background radiation' is also used to describe the microwave radiation left over from 'Big Bang'. This is a different type of radiation to nuclear radiation.

Material can absorb radiation, taking its energy from it. The 'absorbed dose' is the energy transferred per unit mass of the material. The SI unit of absorbed dose is the gray, Gy, for which $1 \text{ Gy} = 1 \text{ J kg}^{-1}$

Radioactive decay occurs when an atomic nucleus changes to a more stable form. This is a random event that cannot be predicted. The emissions from these nuclei are collectively called **radioactivity** or **radiation**.

We are subjected to a constant stream of radiation called **background radiation**. Most of this is 'natural' in the sense that it is not caused by the activities of people. Sources of background radiation include:

- the air that we breathe; radioactive radon gas from rocks can concentrate in buildings
- the ground and buildings; all rocks contain radioactive isotopes
- the food that we eat; the food chain starts with photosynthesis. Radioactive material enters the food chain in the form of carbon-14, an unstable form of carbon that is continually being formed in the atmosphere
- radiation from space, called cosmic radiation
- medical and industrial uses of radioactive materials.

The emissions

AQA A	5	Edexcel context	5
AQA B	5	OCR A	G485
CCEA	A2.1	OCR B	G494
Edexcel concept	5	WJEC	5

The range of a beta-plus particle in ordinary material is effectively zero, since it is annihilated as soon as it collides with an electron.

Alpha radiation is the most intensely ionising and can cause a lot of damage to body tissue. Although the radiation cannot penetrate the skin, alpha emitting isotopes can enter the lungs during breathing.

Radioactive emissions are detected by their ability to cause **ionisation**, creating charged particles from neutral atoms and molecules by removing outer electrons. This results in a transfer of energy from the emitted particle, which is effectively absorbed when all its energy has been lost in this way. The four main emissions are **alpha** (α), **beta-plus** (β^+), **beta-minus** (β^-) and **gamma** (γ). Of these, alpha radiation is the most intensely ionising and has short range while gamma radiation is the least intensely ionising and has the longest range.

- In alpha emission the nucleus emits a particle consisting of two protons and two neutrons. This has the same make-up as a helium nucleus.
- Beta-minus emission occurs when a neutron decays into a proton, emitting an electron in the process.
- In beta-plus emission a proton changes to a neutron by emitting a **positron**, an anti-electron.
- Gamma emission is short wavelength electromagnetic radiation.

Radioactive emission	Nature	Charge/e	Symbol	Penetration	Causes ionisation	Affected by electric and magnetic fields
alpha	two neutrons and two protons	+2	^4_2He or $^4_2\alpha$	absorbed by paper or a few cm of air	intensely	yes
beta-minus	high-energy electron	–1	$^0_{-1}\text{e}$ or $^0_{-1}\beta$	absorbed by 3 mm of aluminium	weakly	yes
beta-plus	positron (antielectron)	+1	$^0_{+1}\text{e}$ or $^0_{+1}\beta$	annihilated by an electron		yes
gamma	short-wavelength electromagnetic radiation	none	$^0_0\gamma$	reduced by several cm of lead	very weakly	no

Notice that the electron emitted in beta-minus decay and the positron emitted in beta-plus decay have been allocated the **atomic numbers** –1 and +1. This is because of the effect on the nucleus when these particles are emitted.

Other types of nuclear decay include:

- **electron capture**, where a proton in the nucleus captures an orbiting electron and becomes a neutron
- **nucleon emission** when some artificially-produced isotopes decay by emitting a proton or a neutron.

Alpha and beta radiations are the most intensely ionising but they are readily absorbed and so easy to shield. Gamma radiation only reacts weakly with matter and is very penetrating. One of the safest ways of protecting against danger from gamma radiation is to maximise the distance from the source to any people. The radiation from a gamma point source is emitted equally in all directions, so the intensity decreases as an inverse square law.

In this context, intensity means the number of photons detected per square metre.

> **KEY POINT**
>
> The intensity, I, of gamma radiation detected from a point source is related to the intensity of the source, I_0, by the equation:
>
> $$I = \frac{kI_0}{x^2}$$
>
> where $k = 1/4\pi$ and x is the distance from the source.

Balanced equations

AQA A	5	Edexcel context	5
AQA B	5	OCR A	G485
CCEA	A2.1	OCR B	G494
Edexcel concept	5	WJEC	5

When a nucleus decays by alpha or beta emission, the numbers of protons and neutrons are changed. Gamma emission does not change the make-up of the nucleus, but corresponds to the nucleus losing excess energy. Gamma emission often occurs alongside alpha and beta emissions, though some artificial radioactive isotopes emit gamma radiation only.

Technetium-99 is an artificial isotope that emits gamma radiation only. It is used as a tracer in medicine. The gamma radiation can be detected outside the body and there is less risk of cell damage than with an isotope that also emits alpha or beta radiation.

The changes that take place due to alpha and beta emissions are:

- **alpha**; the number of protons decreases by 2 and the number of neutrons also decreases by two
- **beta-minus**; the number of neutrons decreases by one and the number of protons increases by one
- **beta-plus**; the number of neutrons increases by one and the number of protons decreases by one.

In writing equations that describe nuclear decay, both charge (represented by the atomic number, Z) and the number of nucleons (represented by the mass number, A) are conserved. The table summarises these changes and gives examples of each type of decay.

Check that the equations given as examples are balanced in terms of charge and number of nucleons.

Particle emitted	Effect on A	Efect on Z	Example
alpha	–4	–2	$^{226}_{88}\text{Ra} \rightarrow {}^{222}_{86}\text{Rn} + {}^{4}_{2}\text{He}$
beta-minus	unchanged	+1	$^{14}_{6}\text{C} \rightarrow {}^{14}_{7}\text{N} + {}^{0}_{-1}\text{e} + \bar{\nu}$
beta-plus	unchanged	–1	$^{11}_{6}\text{C} \rightarrow {}^{11}_{5}\text{B} + {}^{0}_{+1}\text{e} + \nu$

$\bar{\nu}$ is an anti-neutrino. ν is a neutrino.

Rate of decay and half-life

AQA A	5	Edexcel context	5
AQA B	5	OCR A	G485
CCEA	A2.1	OCR B	G494
Edexcel concept	5	WJEC	5

> **KEY POINT**
>
> The activity, or rate of decay, of a sample of radioactive material is measured in **becquerel** (Bq). An activity of 1 Bq represents a rate of decay of 1 s^{-1}.

Radioactive decay is a random process and the decay of an individual nucleus cannot be predicted. However, given a sample containing large numbers of undecayed nuclei, then statistically the rate of decay should be proportional to the number of undecayed nuclei present. Double the size of the sample and, on the average, the rate of decay should also double.

There are only two factors that determine the rate of decay of a sample of radioactive material. They are:

- the radioactive isotope involved
- the number of undecayed nuclei.

> Unlike chemical reactions, radioactive decay is not affected by changes in temperature.

KEY POINT

The relationship between the rate of decay, or activity, of a radioactive isotope and the number of undisclosed nuclei is:

activity, $A = \lambda N$

Where the activity is measured in becquerel, N is the number of undecayed nuclei present and λ is the **decay constant** of the substance. λ has units of s^{-1}.

When the activity of a radioactive isotope (after deducting the average background count) is plotted against time, the result is a curve that shows the activity decreasing as the number of undecayed nuclei decreases. A decay curve is shown in the diagram.

> The graph shown is a plot of activity against time. A plot of number of undecayed nuclei against time would be identical but with a different scale on the *y*-axis.

The shape of the curve is the same for all radioactive substances, but the activities and time scales depend on the size of the sample and its decay constant.

> The negative sign is needed here because the *rate of change of undecayed nuclei* is always negative due to the decrease in the numbers of undecayed nuclei with increasing time.

KEY POINT

An alternative way of expressing activity is *the rate of change of the number of undecayed nuclei with time*:

$$\frac{\Delta N}{\Delta t} = -\lambda N$$

this leads to the relationship between the number of undecayed nuclei, N, and the number at time $t = 0$, N_0:

$$N = N_0 e^{-\lambda t}$$

The curve on the graph above shows **exponential decay**. In an exponential decay curve:

- the rate of change of y, represented by the gradient of the curve, is proportional to y
- in equal intervals of x the value of y always changes in the same ratio.

This second point means that it always takes the same time interval for the activity to decrease to a given fraction of any particular value. The time for the activity to halve is the **half-life** of the substance.

> **KEY POINT**
>
> The half-life of a radioactive isotope, $t_{1/2}$ is the average time taken for the number of undecayed nuclei of the isotope to halve.

Because radioactive decay is a random process, the results of experiments to measure activity may not fit the curve exactly and there is some variation in the change of activity when identical samples of the same material are compared. This is why the term *average* is used in the definition of half-life.

The values of half-lives range from tiny fractions of a second to many millions of years. Starting with N nuclei of a particular isotope, the number remaining after one half-life has elapsed is N/2, after two half-lives N/4 and after n half-lives it is $N/2^n$.

There is a relationship between the half-life and the decay constant of any particular radioactive isotope. The shorter the half-life, the greater the rate of decay and the decay constant.

> **KEY POINT**
>
> The half-life of a radioactive isotope and its decay constant are related by the equation:
> $$\lambda t_{1/2} = \ln 2 = 0.69$$

Stable and unstable nuclei

AQA A	5	Edexcel context	5
AQA B	5	OCR A	G485
CCEA	A2.1	OCR B	G494
Edexcel concept	5	WJEC	5

Carbon-11, carbon-12 and carbon-14 are three isotopes of carbon. Of these, only carbon-12 is stable. It has equal numbers of protons and neutrons. The graph shows the relationship between the number of neutrons (N) and the number of protons (Z) for stable nuclei.

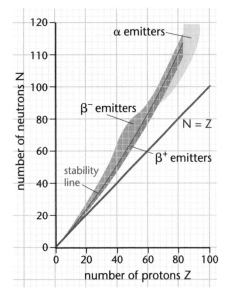

It can be seen from this graph that the condition for a nucleus to be stable depends on the number of protons:

- for values of Z up to about 20, a stable nucleus has equal numbers of protons and neutrons
- for values of Z greater than 20, a stable nucleus has more neutrons than protons.

Unstable nuclei above the stability line in the diagram are **neutron-rich**; they can become more stable by decreasing the number of neutrons. They decay by β⁻ emission; this leads to one less neutron and one extra proton and brings the neutron–proton ratio closer to, or equal to, one. An example is:

$$^{24}_{11}Na \rightarrow\ ^{24}_{12}Mg +\ ^{0}_{-1}e + \bar{v}$$

Unstable nuclei below the stability line decay by β⁺ emission; this increases the neutron number by one at the expense of the proton number. An example is:

$$^{11}_{6}C \rightarrow\ ^{11}_{5}B +\ ^{0}_{+1}e + v$$

The emission of an alpha particle has little effect on the neutron–proton ratio for isotopes that are close to the *N=Z* line and is confined to the more massive nuclei. For these nuclei, emission of an alpha particle changes the balance of the proton–neutron ratio in the favour of the neutrons. In the decay of thorium-228 shown below, the neutron–proton ratio increases from 1.53 to 1.55.

$$^{228}_{90}Th \rightarrow\ ^{224}_{88}Ra +\ ^{4}_{2}He$$

The N=Z line corresponds to a neutron:proton ratio of 1. As an alpha particle consists of two neutrons and two protons, its emission would hardly affect a neutron:proton ratio that is nearly 1.

Progress check

1 What is the effect on atomic and mass number of decay by:
   a an alpha particle only
   b a beta-minus particle only
   c a gamma photon only?

2 Technetium-99 is a gamma emitter with a half-life of 6 hours.
   A fresh sample is prepared with an activity *A*.
   a Calculate the activity of the sample when 24 hours have elapsed since its preparation.
   b Calculate the decay constant of technetium-99.

3 Complete the equation for the decay of phosphorus–32 by beta-minus emission.
   $$^{32}_{15}P \rightarrow S+$$

1 a The atomic number decreases by 2 and the mass number decreases by 4.
   b The atomic number increases by 1 and the mass number is unchanged.
   c Both the atomic number and the mass number are unchanged.
2 a A/16
   b $3.2 \times 10^{-5}\ s^{-1}$
3 $^{32}_{15}P \rightarrow\ ^{32}_{16}S +\ ^{0}_{-1}e$

3.4 Energy from the nucleus

After studying this section you should be able to:

- represent nuclear reactions by nuclear equations
- explain the equivalence of mass and energy
- describe how energy from the nucleus is released in a fission reactor

The nucleus

AQA A	5	Edexcel context	4
AQA B	5	OCR A	G485
CCEA	A2.1	WJEC	5
Edexcel concept	4		

If the size of an atom is compared to that of a cathedral or a football stadium, the nucleus is about the size of a tennis ball. Evidence of the size of the nucleus comes from alpha particle scattering experiments (see page 105).

There are two types of particle in the nucleus, protons and neutrons.

> You will not find El in the periodic table – it is fictitious.

KEY POINT

The nucleus of an element is represented as ^A_ZEl.

Z is the atomic number, the number of protons.

A is the mass number, the number of nucleons (protons and neutrons).

The element is fixed by Z, the number of protons. A neutral atom has equal numbers of protons in the nucleus and electrons in orbit. Different atoms of the same element can have different values of A due to having more or fewer neutrons. As this does not affect the number of electrons in a neutral atom, the chemical properties of these atoms are the same. They are called isotopes of the element.

The most common form of carbon, for example, is carbon-12, $^{12}_6C$, which has six protons and six neutrons in the nucleus. Carbon-14, $^{14}_6C$, has the same number of protons but two extra neutrons. These two forms of carbon are isotopes of the same element.

Atomic mass and energy conservation

AQA A	5	Edexcel context	5
AQA B	5	OCR A	G485
CCEA	A2.1	OCR B	G494
Edexcel concept	4	WJEC	5

The charges and relative masses of atomic particles are shown in the table. The masses are in atomic mass units (u), where 1u = 1/12 the mass of a carbon-12 atom = 1.661×10^{-27} kg. The charges are relative to the value of the electronic charge, e = 1.602×10^{-19} C.

> The phrase 'relative to the value' means compared to the actual amount of charge, ignoring the sign.

Atomic particle	Mass	Charge
proton	1.0073	+1
neutron	1.0087	0
electron	5.49×10^{-4}	−1

A carbon-12 nucleus consists of six protons and six neutrons. The mass of the atom is precisely 12u, by definition, so after taking into account the mass of the electrons, that of the nucleus is 11.9967u. The mass of the constituent neutrons and protons is:

$$6\,m_p + 6\,m_n = 6(1.0073\,u + 1.0087\,u) = 12.0960\,u$$

The nucleus has less mass than the particles that make it up. This appears to contravene the principle of conservation of mass. Einstein established that *energy has mass*. The mass that you gain due to your increased energy when you walk upstairs is infinitesimally small, but at a nuclear level mass changes cannot be ignored. Any change in energy is accompanied by a change in mass, and *vice versa*.

Try using Einstein's equation to calculate the increase in your mass when you climb upstairs to see how small it is.

KEY POINT

Einstein's equation relates the change in energy, ΔE, to the change in mass, Δm

$$\Delta E = \Delta m c^2$$

where c is the speed of light.

It applies to **all** energy changes.

When dealing with the nucleus and nuclear particles, energy and mass are so closely linked that their equivalence, and that of their units, has been established.

KEY POINT

$$1 \text{ u} = 931.5 \text{ MeV}$$

where 1 eV (one electron volt) is the energy transfer when an electron moves through a potential difference of 1 volt.

Using this relationship, the separate conservation rules regarding mass and energy can be combined into one so that (mass + energy) is always conserved in nuclear interactions.

To split a nucleus up into its constituent nucleons requires energy. It follows that a nucleus has less energy than the sum of the energies of the corresponding number of free neutrons and protons. So the fact that a nucleus has less energy than its nucleons would have in isolation means that it also has less mass.

A common misconception is that the binding energy is the energy that holds a nucleus together. It is the energy needed to split it up.

KEY POINT

The difference between the sum of the masses of the individual nucleons and the mass of the nucleus is called the **mass defect**. The matching quantity of energy is called **nuclear binding energy**. It represents the energy required to separate a nucleus into its individual nucleons.

In the case of carbon-12 the mass defect, or nuclear binding energy, is equal to $0.093 \text{ u} = 89.3 \text{ MeV}$.

As would be expected, the greater the number of nucleons, the greater the binding energy. The diagram shows how the binding energy per nucleon varies with nucleon number. The most stable nuclei have the greatest binding energy per nucleon.

Binding energy (or mass defect) can be thought of as the source of the energy that is made available by fission and fusion. Note that an *increase* in binding energy corresponds to a *release* of energy.

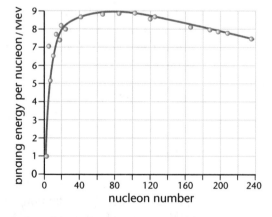

Joining and splitting

The nuclear reaction that releases energy in stars like our Sun is fusion.

In a fusion reaction:

* small nuclei join together to form larger, more massive ones
* the nucleus formed in fusion has less mass than those that fuse together, due to its greater binding energy per nucleon
* the mass difference is released as energy.

Despite some scientists' claims to have carried out 'cold fusion' reactions, these have not been verified.

Fusion reactions can only take place at high temperatures where the nuclei have enough thermal energy to come together despite the repulsive forces that act as they approach each other.

Large nuclei may release energy by **fission**.

In **fission**:

- a large nucleus splits into two smaller ones and two or three neutrons
- the particles formed from fission have less mass than the original nucleus, due to the greater binding energy per nucleon
- the mass difference is released as kinetic energy of the fission fragments.

Induced fission

AQA A	5	Edexcel context	5
AQA B	5	OCR A	G485
CCEA	A2.1	OCR B	G494
Edexcel concept	5	WJEC	5

In a neutron-rich nucleus the neutron–proton ratio is greater than that required for stability.

A thermal neutron has energy similar to the mean kinetic energy of neutrons at room temperature.

Fission can occur spontaneously in a neutron-rich nucleus or it can be caused to take place by changing the make-up of a nucleus so that it is neutron-rich. This is known as **induced fission**.

Induced fission is triggered when a large nucleus absorbs a neutron. A slow-moving, or thermal, neutron has the right amount of energy to cause the fission of uranium-235.

When uranium-235 undergoes fission:

- a nucleus of $^{235}_{92}U$ absorbs a neutron to become $^{236}_{92}U$
- the resulting nucleus is unstable and splits into two approximately equal-sized smaller nuclei, together with two or three neutrons
- a large amount of energy, approximately 200 MeV, is released as kinetic energy.

The fission of uranium-235 is illustrated in the diagram.

before   after

neutron

The fission of uranium-235

Check that this equation is balanced in terms of both mass and charge.

When uranium-235 fissions, the nuclei formed are not always the same. The equation represents one possible reaction, the products being barium and krypton.

$$^{235}_{92}U + ^{1}_{0}n \rightarrow ^{144}_{56}Ba + ^{90}_{36}Kr + 2^{1}_{0}n$$

Releasing the energy

AQA A	5	Edexcel context	5
AQA B	5	OCR A	G485
CCEA	A2.1	OCR B	G494
Edexcel concept		WJEC	5

If the neutrons released from fission go on to cause further fissions, then a **chain reaction** can build up. This is illustrated in the diagram overleaf.

If every neutron produced were to cause the fission of another uranium-235 nucleus, the reaction would quickly go out of control. This does not happen with a small quantity of uranium, since the neutrons produced in the fission process are moving at high speeds. These high-speed neutrons:

- are not as likely to be absorbed by uranium-235 nuclei as thermal neutrons are
- have a good chance of leaving the material altogether due to the relatively large surface of a small mass of material.

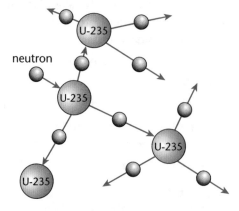

A chain reaction

The atomic bomb dropped on Hiroshima was detonated by combining three small masses of uranium into one that was above the critical mass.

For a stable chain reaction to be sustained then, on average, the neutrons released from each fission must go on to cause one further fission. The minimum mass of material needed for this to happen is called the **critical mass**. For uranium-235, the critical mass is 15 kg. This amount of uranium-235 in a spherical shape (so that it has the minimum surface area) can just sustain a reaction without it dying out.

Harnessing the energy

AQA A	5	OCR A	G485
AQA B	5	OCR B	G494
CCEA	A2.1	WJEC	5

In a **nuclear reactor**, energy released from fission is removed and used to generate electricity. Three important features of a reactor are the **moderator**, **control rods**, and **coolant**. These are shown in the diagram.

This type of reactor is called a thermal reactor as it uses thermal neutrons to cause fission.

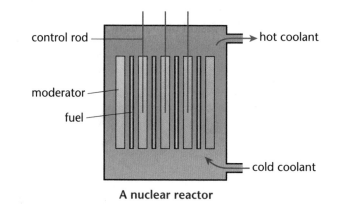

A nuclear reactor

The moderator:

- slows down the high-speed neutrons released by fission so that they are more likely to cause further fissions
- should not absorb neutrons.

Deuterium, ^2_1H, is an isotope of hydrogen that contains an extra neutron.

Graphite and heavy water, similar to normal water but using deuterium in place of hydrogen, are commonly used as moderators. Normal water is unsuitable as the hydrogen nuclei absorb neutrons.

The control rods:

- are used to control the neutron concentration by absorbing neutrons
- can be raised or lowered within the moderator material to increase or decrease the rate at which fissions take place
- must be able to absorb neutrons without becoming unstable.

The material used for control rods needs to have nuclei that are successful at capturing neutrons. Cadmium and boron are both used as they can capture neutrons over a large effective cross-section of their nuclei.

The coolant:

- should flow easily
- should not corrode the metal casings of the moderator and fuel rods
- removes energy to a heat exchanger, where steam is generated to turn turbines as in a coal-fired power station.

The coolant used depends on the temperature of the reactor core. Coolants in use include water, carbon dioxide and liquid sodium.

Nuclear fuels

AQA A	5	OCR A	G485
AQA B	5	OCR B	G495
CCEA	A2.1	WJEC	5

Fast-breeder reactors use **fast** neutrons and **breed** their own fuel.

The first nuclear power stations to be built used natural uranium as a fuel. Natural uranium contains less than 1% uranium-235, the remainder being uranium-238 which does not fission readily. Enriched uranium fuel contains a higher proportion of uranium-235, up to 3%, so it has a longer usable lifetime than natural uranium. Fast-breeder reactors use the plutonium, $^{239}_{94}$Pu, formed when uranium-238, $^{238}_{92}$U, captures a neutron and then decays by β^- emission (twice). Plutonium needs fast neutrons to fission, but the spare neutrons left over from the fission process are used to create more plutonium fuel from uranium-238, so they make their own fuel from the relatively abundant isotope of uranium, uranium-238.

Safety

AQA A	5	OCR A	G485
AQA B	5	OCR B	G495
CCEA	A2.1	WJEC	5

No technology is totally safe. The coolant and other materials used in building a nuclear reactor become radioactive. The products of fission, or daughter nuclei, are also radioactive. Complete removal of the control rods results in a melt-down, as happened at Chernobyl. This released vast quantities of radioactive material into the atmosphere, having disastrous effects in the immediate vicinity and affecting farmland thousands of miles away.

In normal use a thick concrete wall built around the reactor shields the outside environment by absorbing much of the radiation emitted within. In an emergency, a reactor can be shut down by lowering the control rods fully so that they absorb more neutrons, leaving insufficient neutrons to maintain the chain reaction.

The way in which active waste materials are disposed of depends on the level of radioactivity.

Spent fuel rods contain highly radioactive materials with long half-lives. There is no safe way of disposing of these.

- Low-level waste, such as laboratory clothing and packaging, is buried underground or at sea.
- Medium-level waste, such as empty fuel casing and parts of the reactor fabrication, is kept in a concrete-lined store or underground cavern.
- High-level waste, such as the radioactive fission daughter-products and spent fuel rods, is kept in steel tanks of water to keep it cool.

Artificial isotopes

AQA A	5	OCR A	G485
AQA B	5	OCR B	G495
CCEA	A2.1	WJEC	5

Many naturally-occurring radioactive isotopes have long half-lives and so are not suitable for use as tracers in the environment or in the body. Man-made radioactive isotopes can be produced in two ways:

- in a nuclear reactor, by irradiating a stable isotope with neutrons
- by firing charged particles at a stable isotope using a particle accelerator.

The resulting change in the nucleus is known as artificial transmutation. An isotope used extensively in medicine is a form of technetium-99, ^{99}Tc^m, which emits gamma radiation only and has a half-life of 6 hours. It is formed when molybdenum-99, artificially created in a reactor, decays by beta-emission. This form of technetium-99 is particularly useful in medical diagnosis because:

- the gamma radiation can be detected outside the body using a gamma camera
- it does not emit the more intensely-ionising alpha and beta radiations which could cause cell damage
- the half-life is long enough for it to be detected for several hours after being injected and allowed to circulate the body
- the half-life is short enough for a minimum dose to be used
- by attaching the technetium-99 to different substances, it can be targeted towards specific body organs.

The shorter the half-life, the greater the rate of decay so the smaller the dose needed to be detectable.

More about nuclear fusion

The graph on page 100 shows that there is a much larger increase in binding energy per nucleon when two small nuclei fuse than when two large ones split. Fusion can release a lot of energy from a small mass of material. Also, the raw fuel can be hydrogen. So the potential of fusion as a future source of energy is enormous.

The technical problems, however, are also considerable. Nuclei repel each other by electric force, so only at very high temperatures (such as in the Sun or in a 'hydrogen bomb' that is triggered by an initial fission explosion) can they be made to join together. Containing fusing material is very difficult, and can only be done using magnetic fields, with the material in the form of a plasma (ionised). The JET project is a European project that is working to overcome the difficulties, using deuterium ($_1^2$H) and tritium ($_1^3$H) as the fusing materials.

Progress check

1 4.0×10^5 J of energy is transferred to some water in a kettle to bring it to the boil.
   Calculate the increase in mass of the water due to this energy transfer.

2 Describe the difference between nuclear *fusion* and nuclear *fission*.

3 Explain why a fast-breeder reactor does not need a moderator.

3 Fission is caused by fast neutrons, so they do not need to be slowed down.
Fission is the splitting up of a nucleus.
2 Fusion is the joining together of two nuclei.
1 4.4×10^{-12} kg

3.5 Probing matter

After studying this section you should be able to:

- *describe how the scattering of alpha particles and high-energy electrons gives evidence for the atomic model*
- *understand that electron diffraction enables measurements of atomic spacing to be made*
- *relate the four forces (gravitational force, electromagnetic force, strong and weak nuclear forces) to behaviour of matter*
- *explain that quarks, electrons and neutrinos are fundamental particles with antiparticles*
- *explain that hadrons are made of quarks, and name examples of hadrons*
- *describe the roles of exchange particles, including photons, gravitons, gluons, pions and intermediate vector bosons, in all forces between bodies*
- *use Feynman diagrams to represent particle exchange*

Evidence for the atomic model

AQA A	5	Edexcel context	4
AQA B	5	OCR A	G485
CCEA	A2.2	OCR B	G495
Edexcel concept	4		

An alpha particle is a positively-charged particle consisting of two protons and two neutrons.

The experiments were carried out in a vacuum so that the alpha particles were not scattered by air particles.

The simple atomic model pictures the atom as a tiny, positively-charged nucleus surrounded by negatively-charged particles (electrons) in orbit. Evidence for this model comes from the **scattering** of **alpha particles** as they pass through a thin material such as gold foil. The results of these experiments, first carried out under the guidance of Rutherford in 1911, can be summarised as:

- most of the alpha particles travel straight through the foil with little or no deflection
- a small number are deflected by a large amount
- a tiny number are scattered backwards.

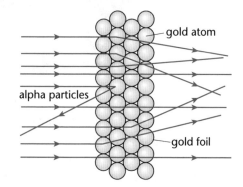

Rutherford concluded that the atoms of gold are mainly empty space, with tiny regions of concentrated charge. This charge must be the same sign as that of alpha particles (positive) to explain the **back-scattering** as being due to the repulsion between similar-charged objects.

The size of the nucleus

AQA A	5	Edexcel context	4
AQA B	5	OCR A	G485
CCEA	A2.2	OCR B	G495
Edexcel concept	4		

Rutherford's experiments established the existence of a nucleus that is very small compared to an atom. They also enabled the first estimates of the size of a nucleus to be made. When an alpha particle is scattered back along its original path:

- as it approaches the nucleus its kinetic energy is transferred to potential energy due to its position in the electric field
- at the closest distance of approach all its energy is potential

It is a maximum value as the nucleus cannot be larger than this but is probably smaller, as the repulsive force reverses the direction of motion of the alpha particles before they reach the nucleus.

- the energy transfer is reversed as it moves away from the nucleus.

The closest distance of approach to the nucleus is therefore calculated from the kinetic energy of the alpha particle, assuming that Coulomb's law applies to the nucleus. This gives a maximum value for the size of the gold nucleus of about 10^{-14} m.

Electron diffraction

AQA A   5
CCEA   A2.2

More precise evidence comes from the scattering of electrons, known as **electron diffraction**. Moving electrons show wave-like behaviour (see section 3.7) with a wavelength that depends on their speed.

Electrons accelerated through a potential difference of a few hundred volts have a wavelength similar to that of X-rays and gamma rays.

This wavelength is also similar to the spacing of the atoms in crystalline materials, so these materials provide suitable sized 'gaps' to cause diffraction.

Diffraction patterns formed by a beam of electrons after passing through thin foil or graphite show a set of 'bright' and 'dark' rings on photographic film, similar to those formed by **X-ray diffraction** (see below).

Analysis of these patterns is used to calculate the spacing between rows of atoms in the sample. This is typically around 10^{-10} m.

Higher energy electrons are used to estimate the size of a nucleus. Electrons accelerated through a voltage of a few hundred million volts have a wavelength comparable to that of a nuclear diameter.

When probing matter, the choice of particle used depends on its interaction with the matter being probed.

Unlike alpha particles, electrons are not repelled as they approach a nucleus. Instead, they are diffracted in the same way that light is diffracted around a circular or spherical obstacle and a diffraction pattern similar to that shown in the diagram above emerges, with the rings having fuzzy edges.

Analysis of the diffraction pattern gives a nuclear size of about 10^{-15} m.

The results of electron diffraction experiments show that:

Unlike their nuclei, the atoms of different elements can have different densities, and differences in inter-atomic spacing result in a huge range of material densities.

- all nuclei have approximately the same density, about 1×10^{17} kg m^{-3}
- the greater the number of nucleons, the larger the radius of the nucleus
- the nucleon number, A, is proportional to the cube of the **nuclear radius, R**.

An alternative way of writing this last point is:

the nuclear radius, R, is proportional to the cube root of the nucleon number, A.

KEY POINT

The relationship between nucleon number, A, and nuclear radius, R, is:
$$R = r_0 A^{1/3}$$
where r_0 has the value 1.2×10^{-15} m.

This relationship means that if the nuclei of ^{64}Cu and ^{32}S are compared, the radius of the copper nucleus is $2^{1/3} = 1.26$ times that of the sulphur, as the nucleon number of copper is twice that of sulphur. Similarly, the copper nucleus has a radius which is $4^{1/3} = 1.59$ times that of ^{16}O.

Nature's four forces

CCEA	A2.2
OCR A	G485

On the nuclear scale, gravitational forces are so weak that they can be ignored.

The strong force decreases very rapidly with increasing separation of the particles.

The word 'particle' is now used for comparatively huge bodies such as molecules as well as 'fundamental' bodies that can't be split into anything smaller, such as electrons.

The forces that we experience every day can be classified as one of two types:

- **gravitational forces** affect all objects that have mass – they are very weak and have an infinite range
- **electromagnetic forces** also have an infinite range and are much stronger than gravitational forces – they include all forces due to static or moving charges. We are less conscious of these forces because everyday matter on the human scale has equal quantities of positive and negative charges.

The nucleus is very concentrated in terms of both mass and charge. The electrostatic force between the protons is immense and the gravitational attraction is tiny, so if these were the only forces acting, the nucleus would be unstable. In addition to the forces above, there are two other fundamental forces.

- The **strong nuclear force** affects protons and neutrons but not electrons. Its limited range, 1×10^{-15} m, means that it only acts between nucleons that are very close, i.e. next to each other in the nucleus.
- The **weak nuclear force** affects all particles. It has an even shorter range than the strong force, 1×10^{-18} m, and is responsible for beta decay.

It is the strong nuclear force that keeps the nucleus together. The strong attraction between the nucleons balances the electrostatic repulsion.

Fundamental and non-fundamental particles

CCEA	A2.2	Edexcel context	4
Edexcel concept	4	OCR A	G485

In an inelastic collision, kinetic energy is not conserved.

Electrons are **fundamental** particles. They cannot be split up. Protons and neutrons are themselves made up of other particles so they are not fundamental. Evidence for the structure of protons and neutrons comes from **deep inelastic scattering** experiments. In these experiments, very-high-energy electrons are fired at nucleons. The electrons are not affected by the strong force and they penetrate the nucleons in an inelastic collision, resulting in the electrons being scattered through a range of angles, with some being back-scattered in the same way that alpha particles can be back-scattered by gold foil.

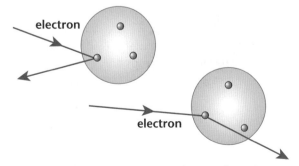

Deep inelastic scattering experiments show that nucleons contain small regions of intense charge.

This gives evidence that a nucleon contains small, dense regions of charge that are themselves fundamental particles. These particles are called **quarks**. The diagram above illustrates some of the findings of deep inelastic scattering. In the diagram below each nucleon is shown as containing three quarks.

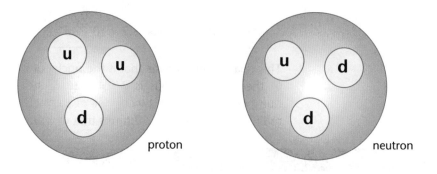

proton   neutron

The quarks contained in nucleons

> The symbol e is used throughout this section to represent the amount of charge on an electron, ignoring the sign. Positive (+) and negative (–) show the sign of a charge.

Of the six types of quark, two occur in protons and neutrons. These are the **up** and **down** quarks. The up quark, symbol u, has a charge of $+\frac{2}{3}e$ and that on the down quark, symbol d, is $-\frac{1}{3}e$. The diagram above shows the quarks in a proton and a neutron.

Particles and their antis

AQA A	5	Edexcel context	4	
AQA B	5	OCR A	G485	
CCEA	A2.2	OCR B	G495	
Edexcel concept	4			

> Where a particle has zero charge, for example the neutron, its antiparticle also has zero charge.

For every type of particle there is an antiparticle. An antiparticle:

- has the same mass as the particle, but has the opposite charge if it is the antiparticle of a charged particle
- annihilates its particle when they collide, the collision resulting in energy in the form of gamma radiation or the production of other particles. This process is called **pair annihilation**
- can be created, along with its particle, when a gamma ray passes close to a nucleus. This process is called **pair production**.

Anti-electrons, or **positrons**, are emitted in some types of radioactive decay and can be created when cosmic rays interact with the nuclei of atoms. Like all antiparticles, they cannot exist for very long on Earth before being annihilated by the corresponding particles.

> The symbols β^- and β^+ are normally used to refer to electrons and positrons given off as a result of radioactive decay.

KEY POINT

Using symbols for particles

An electron is represented by the symbol e^- or β^-.

The positron can be represented by either of the symbols e^+ and β^+.

The proton and antiproton are written as p^+ and p^-.

More generally, a line drawn above the symbol for a particle refers to an antiparticle, so u and $\bar{u}$ (read as u-bar) refer to the up quark and its antiquark.

> The greek letter ν is pronounced as 'new'.

The **antineutrino**, $\bar{\nu}$, is a particle of antimatter emitted along with an electron when a nucleus undergoes β^- decay. It is a particle that has almost no mass and no charge. Its corresponding particle the **neutrino**, ν, is emitted with a positron in β^+ decay.

The quark family

CCEA   A2.2   Edexcel context   4
Edexcel concept   4   OCR A   G485

There are six quarks which, together with their antiquarks, make up the quark family. The name of each quark describes its type, or **flavour**. Some of the properties of quarks are:

- charge – this is $+\frac{2}{3}e$ or $-\frac{1}{3}e$ for quarks and is always conserved
- baryon number – like charge, this is conserved in all interactions
- strangeness – this property describes the strange behaviour of some particles that contain quarks. It is conserved in strong and electromagnetic interactions but can be changed in weak interactions.

The values of these properties are shown in the table.

The six quarks can be thought of as three pairs, u–d, c–s and t–b.

Quark	Symbol	Charge/e	Baryon number, B	Strangeness, S
up	u	$+\frac{2}{3}$	$\frac{1}{3}$	0
down	d	$-\frac{1}{3}$	$\frac{1}{3}$	0
charm	c	$+\frac{2}{3}$	$\frac{1}{3}$	0
strange	s	$-\frac{1}{3}$	$\frac{1}{3}$	−1
top	t	$+\frac{2}{3}$	$\frac{1}{3}$	0
bottom	b	$-\frac{1}{3}$	$\frac{1}{3}$	0

The properties of antiquarks are similar to those of the corresponding quark but with the opposite sign, so the antiquark $\bar{s}$ has charge $+\frac{1}{3}$, baryon number $-\frac{1}{3}$.

The hadrons

CCEA   A2.2   Edexcel context   4
Edexcel concept   4   OCR A   G485

The **hadrons** and **leptons** are two groups of particles. Hadrons are affected by both the strong and the weak nuclear force, but leptons are affected by the weak force only.

Hadrons are not fundamental particles; the two types of hadron are made up of quarks:

- **baryons** are made up of three quarks
- **mesons** consist of a quark and an antiquark.

The familiar baryons are the proton, whose quark structure is uud, and the neutron, udd. Protons are particularly stable – they rarely change into anything else. There are other baryons which have different combinations of quarks but they are all unstable and have short lifetimes. All baryons have a baryon number +1, as each quark contributes a baryon number of $+\frac{1}{3}$.

Two families of mesons are the **pi-mesons**, or **pions**, and the **kaons**. Because a meson consists of a quark and an antiquark, it has baryon number 0.

The table shows the structure and some properties of the kaons and pions.

Particle	Structure	Charge/e	Baryon number, B	Strangeness, S
π^0	$u\bar{u}$ or $d\bar{d}$	0	0	0
π^+	$u\bar{d}$	+1	0	0
π^-	$\bar{u}d$	−1	0	0
K^0	$d\bar{s}$	0	0	+1
K^+	$u\bar{s}$	+1	0	+1
K^-	$\bar{u}s$	−1	0	−1

The leptons

| CCEA | | A2.2 | Edexcel context | 4 |
| Edexcel concept | 4 | OCR A | | G485 |

Leptons are fundamental particles. There are three families of leptons:

- the electron and its antiparticle the positron, e^- and e^+, together with the neutrinos given off in β^- and β^+ decay. These neutrinos are called the electron-antineutrino, $\bar{\nu}_e$, and the electron-neutrino, ν_e, to distinguish them from the neutrinos associated with the other leptons
- the muons, μ^- and μ^+, together with their neutrinos ν_μ and $\bar{\nu}_\mu$. Muons have 200 times the mass of electrons, but are unstable, decaying to an electron and a neutrino
- the tauons, τ^- and τ^+ and their neutrinos ν_τ and $\bar{\nu}_\tau$. The tauons are the most massive leptons, having twice the mass of a proton. Like the muons, they are unstable.

> Remember, a fundamental particle cannot be split up into other, simpler particles.

Muons are produced by cosmic rays. Their properties are similar to those of electrons and positrons but they are much more massive. Tauons are the elephants of the lepton tribe; they are produced by the interaction of high-energy electrons and positrons.

Exchanging particles

| CCEA | | A2.2 | Edexcel context | 4 |
| Edexcel concept | 4 | OCR A | | G485 |

The concept of a **field** is used to describe the effects of gravitational and electromagnetic forces and how they vary with distance. This is a useful concept that enables the size and direction of forces to be calculated, but it does not explain what causes them.

The interaction between particles that results in attractive and repulsive forces is due to a continual exchange of other particles. These **exchange particles** have a very short lifetime and owe their existence to borrowed energy, so they are often referred to as **virtual particles**.

There are different exchange particles associated with each of the four fundamental forces. For electromagnetic forces the exchange particles are photons, short bursts of electromagnetic radiation.

> A photon is a 'packet' of electromagnetic radiation.

When two electrons approach each other they exchange virtual photons. The closer the electrons are to each other, the shorter the wavelength of the virtual photons exchanged.

The exchange of virtual photons between two interacting electrons

This exchange of virtual photons results in the electrons moving away from each other in the same way as two ice skaters on a collision course would move away from each other if they were to keep throwing things at each other!

Richard Feynman was an American physicist. He is famous for his books *Lectures on Physics* and for his way of explaining Physics concepts by using diagrams.

The diagram on page 110 represents the exchange of virtual photons between two interacting electrons. Interactions between particles can be represented by **Feynman diagrams**. In these diagrams:

- straight lines are used for the interacting particles
- wavy lines represent the exchange particles
- the straight lines extend beyond the diagram, showing the existence of these particles before and after the interaction
- the wavy lines are contained within the diagram, showing that the exchange particles are short-lived.

This is a Feynman diagram for the interaction between two electrons shown in the diagram on page 110. The arrows do not represent directions of travel: arrows pointing in show the particles before the interaction and those pointing out show the particles after the interaction. The symbol γ is used to represent the exchange of virtual photons.

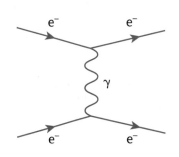

The exchange particles for gravitational forces are called **gravitons**, symbol g, though these have not yet been observed.

The strong force

OCR A   G485

The same symbol, g, is used for both gluons and gravitons.

It is the strong force that holds nucleons together in a nucleus and holds quarks together in a nucleon.

The exchange particles between quarks are called **gluons**, symbol g. The quarks that make up a proton or neutron are constantly exchanging gluons as they interact with each other.

The exchange of gluons between the quarks in a proton

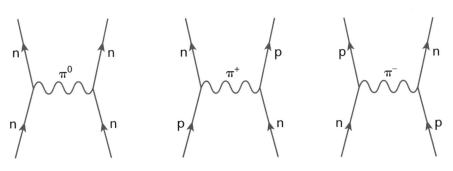

Interactions between nucleons

Pions, or pi-mesons, are responsible for the strong force between nucleons. Two protons or two neutrons exchange pi-zero, π^0, particles, but any one of the three pions can be exchanged during an interaction between a proton and a neutron. Feynman diagrams for some of the possible interactions are shown above.

Notice that charge and baryon number are conserved at each junction of the diagrams.

The weak force

OCR A — G485

The intermediate vector bosons form another group of particles, separate from the hadrons and leptons.

Weak interactions involve the exchange of one of three particles called **intermediate vector bosons**. Like the pi-mesons, their symbols, W^+, W^- and Z^0 indicate the charge on each boson. The W^+ boson carries charge $+e$ and the W^- boson carries charge $-e$.

- The W^+ boson transfers charge $+e$; it is exchanged in an interaction between a neutrino and a neutron, resulting in an electron and a proton.
- The W^- boson is responsible for β^- decay of a neutron.
- Weak interactions where there is no transfer of charge involve the Z^0 boson.

Can you interpret these Feynman diagrams? Try to describe the interaction that each one represents.

Feynman diagrams for these interactions are shown below.

In two of these examples the type or flavour of a quark in the neutron has been changed from d to u by the weak interaction involving a charge-carrying boson. In β^- decay a down quark emits a W^- particle which decays to an electron and its antineutrino. This is shown in the diagram below.

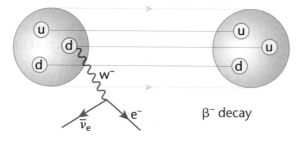

β^- decay

Progress check

1 In alpha particle scattering by a gold nucleus, what feature of the results of the experiment shows that:
   a most of the atom is empty space
   b the nucleus has the same charge as the alpha particles?

2 What is the speed of an alpha particle at its closest distance of approach to a nucleus?

3 Explain why it is more difficult to accelerate neutrons than it is to accelerate electrons.

4 State one piece of evidence for:
   a the particle nature of matter
   b the existence of nuclei.

5 Describe the differences between:
   a hadrons and leptons
   b baryons and mesons.

6 What change takes place in a proton in β^+ decay?

7 a What feature of the results of alpha-particle scattering experiments shows that the nucleus is positively charged?
   b Explain how the results of these experiments suggest that the nucleus occupies a very small proportion of the volume of the atom.

1 a Most of the particles pass through undeviated.
  b Some alpha particles are back-scattered.
2 Zero.
3 Electrons are charged so they can be accelerated by an electric field. Neutrons are uncharged.
4 Possible answers include: a Brownian motion b alpha scattering
5 a Hadrons are made up of quarks.
    Leptons are fundamental particles.
  b Baryons contain 3 quarks. Mesons contain a quark and an antiquark.
6 A u quark changes to a d quark, changing the quark structure of the nucleon from uud to udd.
7 a The fact that some alpha particles are back-scattered shows that they are repelled from the nucleus, so they must have the same charge.
  b Most alpha particles pass through thin gold foil without being deviated.

3.6 Accelerators and detectors

After studying this section you should be able to:

- *describe how a Van de Graaff generator and a linac are used to accelerate particles for firing at fixed targets*
- *explain how a cyclotron is used for colliding beam experiments*
- *explain the principles of operation of particle detectors*

LEARNING SUMMARY

Electron beams

AQA A	5
AQA B	5
CCEA	A2.2
Edexcel concept	4

Electron diffraction investigations require beams of energetic electrons. Cathode ray oscilloscopes and older (vacuum tube) televisions also use electron beams, as do electron microscopes. 'Cathode ray' is an old name for an electron beam.

Beams can be produced by **electron guns**. An electron gun has a heated metal, and the heating provides energy for the escape of some electrons from the metal surface. This is called **thermionic emission**. The metal electron source is given a negative electric charge, and is called a **cathode**.

A metal **anode**, which is not heated, has a positive electric potential. The potential difference between the anode and cathode accelerates the electrons, and if the anode is symmetrical with a fine hole then some electrons pass through this to create a narrow beam. The electric gun is enclosed in a vacuum and the beam can be deflected by electric or magnetic fields.

potential difference. V

A coated screen will glow when hit by the electron beam energy gained by an electron in being $= \frac{1}{2}m_e v^2 = eV$ accelerated from cathode to anode where m_e is electron mass, e is electron charge, v is the acquired velocity.

Van de Graaff generator

CCEA	A2.2

Remember, 1 eV is the energy gained by an electron when accelerated through a potential difference of 1 V.

The **Van de Graaff generator** is used to accelerate particles in a straight line. It is capable of giving them energies up to several MeV. The principle of a high voltage Van de Graaff generator is shown in the diagram.

- Positive ions are sprayed onto a revolving belt at A by a high voltage source which ionises the air and repels positively-charged particles onto the belt.

- A negative charge is induced on the inner surface of the dome, with a positive charge being induced on the outer surface.

- Electrons are sprayed onto the belt at B.

This results in a very high voltage being created between the dome and earth. The voltage can be used to accelerate charged particles by passing them through a series of electrodes connected so that ions pass through them in stages. At each stage the ions are accelerated and focused.

The diagram below shows an arrangement suitable for accelerating negative ions such as electrons. To accelerate positive ions, the potential difference is reversed.

The resistors are used to create a 'step' in potential from each cylinder to the next.

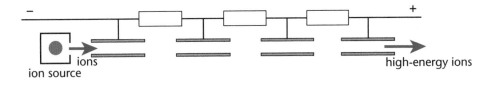

The linac

A **linac** (short for linear accelerator) provides much higher-energy particles than a Van de Graaff machine alone is capable of producing. Charged particles accelerated by a linac can achieve energies of several GeV, at which their speed is approaching that of the speed of light.

No particle can ever reach the speed of light because, according to Einstein's theory, the mass of a particle increases with increasing speed and approaches infinity as its speed approaches that of light.

The diagram below shows a linac that is used to accelerate protons.

In a proton-accelerating linac:

- the protons pass through a large number of cylindrical tubes
- the protons travel at a constant speed within each tube and are accelerated as they pass into the next one
- the acceleration is achieved by a high-frequency, high-voltage alternating potential difference applied to the tubes
- the polarity of the potential difference applied to each tube changes so that the tube that the protons are approaching is negative and the one they are leaving is positive
- each tube is longer than the previous one because the accelerated protons are travelling increasing distances in the time taken for half of one complete cycle of the applied voltage to occur.

As the protons speed up, they travel increasing distances in time 1/2f. This is the time it takes to travel through one tube and pass into the next, where f is the frequency of the voltage supply.

The source of protons is normally a Van de Graaff accelerator, so that the protons entering the linac already have energies of MeV. Linacs that accelerate electrons use high-frequency electromagnetic waves that travel inside metal cavities.

The World's largest linear accelerator is at Stanford in California. It is nearly 4 km long and it can accelerate electrons and positrons to energies of 50 GeV. Linear accelerators:

There are plans to build a new electron-positron linac that will be 30 km long and will accelerate these particles to energies of the order of 10^{13} eV.

- produce a narrow beam of high intensity
- suffer little energy loss from the beam as it travels along the accelerator.

Ring accelerators

Cyclotrons are another kind of accelerator.

The Large Hadron Collider, LHC, at CERN in Switzerland is the latest and most powerful machine developed to probe matter.

Ring accelerators can produce even higher energy particles than linacs currently in use. They can accelerate particles to energies of several thousand GeV.

One major disadvantage of ring accelerators is that the charged particles radiate energy due to the continual change in velocity as they change direction – a problem that does not arise in a linear accelerator.

Targets

Conservation of momentum applies to all collisions, but when the resulting particles have a large amount of momentum, they also have a large amount of kinetic energy.

Energy has mass, and mass-energy is conserved. A loss in kinetic energy results in the mass of that energy appearing elsewhere.

High-energy particles from accelerators are used in the quest for more knowledge and understanding of the behaviour of sub-atomic particles. To achieve this, high-energy particles are fired at targets and then the tracks left by the collision debris are examined.

The particles produced by an accelerator can collide with a **fixed target** or another beam of particles in a **colliding beam experiment**.

A fixed target could be liquid hydrogen or water or a metal such as iridium. In a fixed target experiment:

- conservation of momentum applies to these collisions, so the momentum of the particles after the collision is equal to that of the accelerated particle that collides with the target
- the kinetic energy of the particles formed as a result of the collision comes from that of the accelerated particle
- very little energy, typically only 5%, is available to create new particles.

When beams of particles moving in opposite directions collide:

- conservation of momentum applies, so if the particles have equal masses and speeds their momentum after the collision is zero
- no kinetic energy of the colliding particles remains after the collision, so all of the initial kinetic energy is available to create new particles
- these collisions can result in the creation of a new particle that has no kinetic energy but large mass.

Tracks

Hydrogen is particularly suitable as a target as its nucleus is a single proton.

There are a number of ways of detecting the particles created in high-energy collisions.

In a **cloud chamber**, particles pass through a super-saturated vapour which condenses on the ionised air particles created by collisions, leaving vapour trails.

A similar effect occurs in a **bubble chamber**. Here, the particles pass through a superheated liquid, and bubbles of vapour form in the path of the particle. Liquid hydrogen is often used as it acts both as the fixed target and the detector.

Because the liquid in a bubble chamber is much denser than the gas-vapour mixture in a cloud chamber, collisions are more frequent and high-energy particles are stopped in a shorter distance. A magnetic field applied perpendicular to the plane of the chamber causes charged particles to follow curved paths.

The diagram below shows cloud chamber and bubble chamber tracks.

The energies of the alpha particles can be deduced from the tracks that they leave.

Alpha particle tracks in a cloud chamber

Bubble chamber tracks

These tracks show that:

- the alpha particles in the cloud chamber shown have two different values of energy and momentum
- the bubble chamber shows the tracks left by particles of opposite signs, since there are deflections in opposite directions due to the magnetic field
- there is a range of particle energy and momentum.

A spark is a flash of light emitted when positive ions capture electrons.

In a **spark chamber**, ionising particles cause sparks as they pass between electrodes and ionise an inert gas such as neon. The passage of particles through the chamber can be detected in two ways:

- by photographing the sparks
- by detecting the electrical pulses that pass in the electrodes.

The principle of a spark chamber is shown in the diagram on the right.

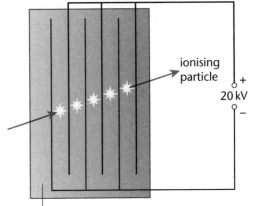

ionising particle

20 kV

neon gas

The track of a particle through a drift chamber is produced by computer analysis of the pulses of current in the wires.

The **drift chamber** is a development of the spark chamber and works on a similar principle. It consists of a mesh of fine wires, each of which is at the opposite potential to its neighbours. A drift chamber:

- takes into account the time taken for ionised particles to reach a wire and be detected
- can pinpoint the position of a particle to within 50 μm
- requires a very pure inert gas
- gives a three-dimensional picture of the track of a particle.

Progress check

1 Explain why the tubes in a linac are of increasing length.

2 Why is there little energy loss from particles in a linac compared to that in a ring accelerator?

3 Suggest why X-rays do not leave tracks in a cloud chamber.

3 X-rays are only weakly ionising.

2 The particles do not radiate energy due to changes in direction.

1 The time taken for the particles to pass from one tube to the next is fixed. As the particles speed up, they travel increasing distances in this time.

3.7 Quantum phenomena

After studying this section you should be able to:

- describe the main features of the electromagnetic spectrum
- explain how the photoelectric effect gives evidence for the particulate nature of electromagnetic radiation
- explain line spectra and relate the spectral lines to energy level transitions

LEARNING SUMMARY

Waves or particles

AQA A	5
AQA B	4
Edexcel concept	4

The **threshold wavelength**, λ_0, is the wavelength of the waves that have the threshold frequency.
$$\lambda_0 = c \div f_0$$

The photoelectric effect can be demonstrated using a zinc plate connected to a gold leaf electroscope. An ultraviolet lamp discharges a negatively-charged plate but has no effect on a positively-charged plate.

The word quantum refers to the smallest amount of a quantity that can exist. A quantum of electromagnetic radiation is the smallest amount of energy of that frequency.

The conversion factor for changing energies in eV to energies in joules is 1.60×10^{-19} J eV^{-1}

The **photoelectric effect** provides evidence that electromagnetic waves have a particle-like behaviour which is more pronounced at the short-wavelength end of the spectrum. In the photoelectric effect electrons are emitted from a metal surface when it absorbs electromagnetic radiation.

The results of photoelectricity experiments show that:

- there is no emission of electrons below a certain frequency, called the **threshold frequency**, f_0, which is different for different metals
- above this frequency, electrons are emitted with a range of kinetic energies up to a maximum, $(\frac{1}{2}mv^2)_{max}$
- increasing the frequency of the radiation causes an increase in the maximum kinetic energy of the emitted electrons, but has no effect on the photoelectric current, i.e. the rate of emission of electrons
- increasing the intensity of the radiation has no effect if the frequency is below the threshold frequency; for frequencies above the threshold it causes an increase in the photoelectric current, so the electrons are emitted at a greater rate.

The wave model cannot explain this behaviour; if electromagnetic radiation is a continuous stream of energy then radiation of all frequencies should cause photoelectric emission. It should only be a matter of time for an electron to absorb enough energy to be able to escape from the attractive forces of the positive ions in the metal.

The explanation for the photoelectric effect relies on the concept of a **photon**, a quantum or packet of energy. We picture electromagnetic radiation as short bursts of energy, the energy of a photon depending on its frequency.

A lamp emits random bursts of energy. Each burst is a photon, a quantum of radiation.

> The relationship between the energy E of a photon, or quantum of electromagnetic radiation, and its frequency, f, is:
> $$E = hf$$
> where h is Planck's constant and has the value 6.63×10^{-34} J s.
>
> *KEY POINT*

The energy of a photon can be measured in either joules or **electronvolts**. The electronvolt is a much smaller unit than the joule.

> One electron volt (1 eV) is the energy transfer when an electron moves through a potential difference of 1 volt.
> $$1 \text{ eV} = 1.60 \times 10^{-19} \text{ J}$$
>
> *KEY POINT*

The work function is the **minimum** energy needed to liberate an electron from a metal. Some electrons need more than this amount of energy.

Radiation below the threshold frequency, f_0, no matter how intense, does not cause any emission of electrons.

Einstein's explanation of photoelectric emission is:

- Light arrives at the metal surface in separate 'packages' or quanta of energy, each with energy hf.
- An electron needs to absorb a minimum amount of energy to escape from a metal. This minimum amount of energy is a property of the metal and is called the **work function**, ϕ.
- If the photons of the incident radiation have energy (hf) less than ϕ then there is no emission of electrons.
- Emission becomes just possible when hf = ϕ.
- For photons with energy greater than ϕ, the electrons emitted have a range of kinetic energies, those with the maximum energy being the ones that needed the minimum energy to escape.
- Increasing the intensity of the radiation increases the number of photons incident each second. This causes a greater rate of emission of electrons, but does not affect their maximum kinetic energy.

> **KEY POINT**
>
> Einstein's photoelectric equation relates the maximum kinetic energy of the emitted electrons to the work function and the energy of each photon:
>
> $$hf = \phi + (\tfrac{1}{2}mv^2)_{max}$$

At the threshold frequency, the minimum frequency that can cause emission from a given metal, $(\tfrac{1}{2}mv^2)_{max}$ is zero and so the equation becomes $hf_0 = \phi$.

Stopping the emission

A stopping potential is positive compared to earth.

The emitting surface can be given positive potential, so that it acts as a positive electrode and attracts the electrons that are emitted from it by photoelectric emission. A second plate above this can act as a negative electrode, repelling the emitted electrons. The potential difference between the plates can be varied. The **stopping potential**, V_s, is the potential difference that is just large enough to prevent even the fastest electron from reaching the negative electrode.

> **KEY POINT**
>
> The **stopping potential** V_s, is the potential difference that just stops the fastest electrons from passing between the emitting surface (which acts as a positive electrode) and a negative electrode.
>
> $$eV_s = (\tfrac{1}{2}mv^2)_{max}$$

Particles or waves

AQA A	5
AQA B	4
Edexcel concept	4
Edexcel context	4

If waves can show particle-like behaviour in photoelectric emission, can particles also behave as waves? Snooker balls bounce off cushions in the same way that light bounces off a mirror, so reflection is not a test for wave-like or particle-like behaviour. Diffraction and interference are properties unique to waves, so particles can be said to have a wave-like behaviour if they show these properties.

Electrons can also be made to interfere when two coherent beams overlap. They produce an interference pattern similar to that of light, but on a much smaller scale.

Other 'particles' such as protons and neutrons also show wave-like behaviour.

Try calculating the de Broglie (pronounced de Broy) wavelength of a moving snooker ball. Is it possible for the ball to show wave-like behaviour?

All particles have an associated wavelength called the **de Broglie** wavelength:

> **KEY POINT**
>
> The wavelength, λ, of a particle is related to its momentum, p, by the de Broglie equation:
>
> $$\lambda = h/p = h/mv$$
>
> where h is the Planck constant.

The de Broglie wavelength of such an electron is of the order of 1×10^{-10} m.

An electron that has been accelerated through a potential difference of a few hundred volts has a wavelength similar to that of X-rays and gamma rays.

This wavelength is also similar to the spacing of the atoms in crystalline materials, so these materials provide suitable sized 'gaps' to cause diffraction.

Particles and waves are the models that we use to describe and explain physical phenomena. It is not surprising that the real world does not fit neatly into our models.

There are two separate models of how matter behaves. The particle model explains such phenomena as ionisation and photoelectricity, while the wave model explains interference and diffraction. It is not appropriate to classify matter absolutely as 'waves' or 'particles' as photons and electrons can fit either model, depending on the circumstances.

Progress check

1 The work function of potassium is 2.84 eV. Calculate:
   a the minimum frequency of radiation that causes photoelectric emission.
   b the maximum energy of the emitted electrons when ultraviolet radiation of frequency 8.40×10^{14} Hz is absorbed by potassium.

2 Calculate the de Broglie wavelength of a neutron, mass = 1.67×10^{-27} kg, travelling at a speed of 200 m s^{-1}.
   h = 6.63×10^{-34} J s

1 a 6.85×10^{14} Hz
  b 1.03×10^{-19} J
2 1.99×10^{-9} m

Sample question and model answer

Radon-220 decays by *alpha-emission* to polonium-216.

(a) Explain what is meant by *alpha-emission*. [2]

> Note that the two marks awarded here are for describing the structure of an alpha particle and describing the emission.

The nucleus emits a particle (1 mark) which consists of two protons and two neutrons (1 mark).

(b) Complete the decay equation, [2]

$$^{220}_{86}\text{Rn} \rightarrow \text{Po} + \text{He}$$

> The nuclear equation should be balanced in terms of both mass (top number) and charge (lower number).

$^{220}_{86}\text{Rn} \rightarrow ^{216}_{84}\text{Po} + ^{4}_{2}\text{He}$ *(1 mark for each correct symbol)*

(c) The graph shows how the activity of a sample of radon-220 changes with time.

(i) Use the graph to determine the half-life of radon-220. [2]

> It is important to take at least two readings here to determine the *average* time for the rate of decay to halve. Had the two readings been different, a third one would be necessary.

time taken for activity to halve from 80 Bq to 40 Bq = 52.5 s **1 mark**
time taken for activity to halve from 40 Bq to 20 Bq = 52.5 s
half-life = average of these readings = 52.5 s **1 mark**

(ii) The relationship between half-life, $t_{\frac{1}{2}}$ and decay constant, λ, is:

$$\lambda\, t_{\frac{1}{2}} = \ln 2$$

> If these relationships are not given in the question, they will be provided on a data sheet. Always check a data sheet, it may contain the formula that you cannot remember!

Calculate the decay constant of radon-220. [2]

$\lambda = \ln 2 \div t_{\frac{1}{2}}$ *(1 mark)* $= \ln 2 \div 52.5\ s = 1.32 \times 10^{-2}\ s^{-1}$ **1 mark**

(iii) The activity, A, of a radioactive sample is related to the number of undecayed nuclei, N, by the formula:

$$A = \lambda N$$

Calculate the number of undecayed nuclei in the sample of radon-220 at time = 0 on the graph. [2]

activity at time t = 0 is 80 Bq **1 mark**
$N = A \div \lambda = 80\ Bq \div 1.32 \times 10^{-2}\ s^{-1} = 6060$ **1 mark**

Practice examination questions

1

The diagram shows how an electric immersion heater can be used to measure the specific heat capacity of a metal block.

(a) (i) What is the advantage of heating the block through a temperature difference of 10 K rather than 1 K? [1]

(ii) What is the advantage of heating the block through a temperature difference of 10 K rather than 100 K? [1]

(iii) Explain whether you would expect the experiment to give a higher value or a lower value than that given in a data book. [2]

(iv) Suggest one way of improving the reliability of the result. [1]

(b) Use the data to calculate a value for the specific heat capacity of the metal. [3]

heater power	= 24 W
time heater switched on	= 350 s
mass of block	= 0.80 kg
initial temperature	= 22°C
final temperature	= 36°C

2

The first law of thermodynamics can be written as:
$$\Delta U = Q + W$$

(a) State the meaning of each symbol in the equation. [3]

(b) As a gas is being compressed, 4500 J of work are done on it and 4800 J of heat are removed from it. Explain what happens to the temperature of the gas as a result of this. [2]

3

The diagram shows a heat engine.

Practice examination questions (continued)

(a) Calculate the efficiency of the heat engine. [2]

(b) What is the maximum efficiency of the engine? [2]

(c) Suggest one reason why the efficiency of the heat engine is less than its theoretical maximum. [1]

4

A sample of an ideal gas has a volume of 2.20×10^{-6} m^3 at a temperature of 25°C and a pressure of 2.02×10^5 Pa.

(a) Calculate the temperature of the gas in kelvin. [1]

(b) Calculate the number of moles of gas in the sample. [3]
$R = 8.3$ J mol^{-1} K^{-1}

(c) The absolute temperature of the gas is doubled, while the pressure remains constant.

   (i) What is meant by the *internal energy* of the gas? [1]
   (ii) In what form is this energy in an ideal gas? [1]
   (iii) What happens to the internal energy of the gas when its absolute temperature is doubled? Explain your answer. [2]
   (iv) Calculate the new volume occupied by the gas after its absolute temperature has doubled and constant pressure. [2]

5

In a nuclear reactor uranium-238, $^{238}_{92}$U, undergoes fission when it captures a neutron.

(a) (i) Write down the symbol for the isotope formed when uranium-238 captures a neutron. [1]
   (ii) Explain what happens when a nucleus of this isotope undergoes fission. [3]
   (iii) Explain how fission can lead to a chain reaction. [2]

(b) (i) Explain why nuclear fission results in the release of energy. [2]
   (ii) In what form is the energy released? [2]
   (iii) Outline how the energy released in fission is used to generate electricity. [3]

(c) State the purpose of each of the following parts of a nuclear reactor:
   (i) control rods [1]
   (ii) moderator. [1]

6

A sample of an ideal gas has a volume of 1.50×10^{-4} m^3 at a temperature of 22°C and a pressure of 1.20×10^5 Pa.

(a) Calculate the temperature of the gas in kelvin. [1]

(b) Calculate the number of moles in the sample.
$R = 8.3$ J mol^{-1}. [3]

(c) If the volume of the gas remains constant, calculate the temperature at which the pressure of the gas is 2.00×10^5 Pa. [3]

(d) (i) Calculate the mean kinetic energy of the gas particles at a temperature of 22°C. The Boltzmann constant, $k = 1.38 \times 10^{-23}$ J K^{-1}. [3]
   (ii) At what temperature would this mean kinetic energy be doubled? Explain how you arrive at your answer. [2]

Practice examination questions *(continued)*

7

Calculate the energy released when 1.8 kg of steam at 100°C is changed into water at 85°C. [3]

specific latent heat of vaporisation of water = 2.25×10^6 J kg^{-1}
specific heat capacity of water   = 4.20×10^3 J kg^{-1} K^{-1}

8

A kettle is filled with 1.50 kg of water at 10°C.
The kettle is fitted with a 2.40 kW heater.
The specific heat capacity of water is 4.2×10^3 J kg^{-1} K^{-1}.

(a) Calculate the time it takes for the water to boil after the kettle is switched on. [3]

(b) Suggest three reasons why the time taken is longer than the answer to (a). [3]

9

Iodine-123 and iodine-131 are two radioactive isotopes of iodine.
Iodine-123 emits gamma radiation only with a half-life of 13 hours.
Iodine-131 emits beta and gamma radiation and has a half-life of 8 days.

Both can be used to monitor the activity of the thyroid gland by measuring the count rate using a detector outside the body.

(a) Which of the radioactive emissions from iodine-131 can be detected outside the body? Give the reason for your answer. [2]

(b) In terms of the radiation emitted, explain why iodine-123 is often preferred to iodine-131. [2]

(c) Explain why a smaller dose is needed when iodine-123 is used than for iodine-131. [2]

(d) A patient is given a dose of iodine-123. After what time interval can medical staff be sure that the activity of the patient's thyroid gland is less than 2% of its greatest value? [2]

10

Information about the size of a nucleus can be obtained by firing high-energy electrons at the nucleus and examining the subsequent diffraction pattern.

(a) (i) Why are electrons suitable for this purpose? [2]
    (ii) Explain why the electrons need to be high-energy. [3]

(b) The relationship between the radius, R, of a nucleus and its atomic number, A is: $R = r_0 A^{1/3}$

where r_0 has the value 1.20×10^{-15} m.

Calculate the radius of the nuclei of:

(i) $^4_2$He [2]

(ii) $^{32}_{16}$S [1]

(c) Explain what the answers to (b) show about the densities of the helium and sulphur nuclei. [3]

Practice examination questions *(continued)*

11

The diagram shows some of the results of firing alpha particles at gold foil.

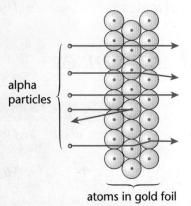

alpha particles

atoms in gold foil

Explain how each of the following provides evidence for the atomic model.

(a) Most alpha particles pass through the foil undeviated. [2]

(b) A very small number of alpha particles are scattered backwards. [3]

12

Einstein's equation for photoelectric emission is:

$$hf = \Phi + (\tfrac{1}{2}mv^2)_{max}$$

(a) (i) State the meaning of each term. [3]

(ii) What is the significance of the subscript 'max'? [1]

(b) Electromagnetic radiation of frequency 2.02×10^{15} Hz is directed at a metal surface. The maximum kinetic energy of the electrons emitted is 4.05×10^{-19} J. The intensity of the radiation is 4.5 µW m^{-2}.

Calculate:

(i) the energy of each photon [2]

(ii) the number of photons reaching the surface each second if the area is 2.5×10^{-6} m^2 [2]

(iii) The work function of the metal. Give your answer in eV. [3]

Chapter 4

Further physics

The following topics are covered in this chapter:

- Physics of the senses
- Medical and geophysical imaging

- Starlight
- The expanding Universe

4.1 Physics of the senses

After studying this section you should be able to:

- *use ray diagrams and the lens formula to describe image formation by lenses*
- *explain how the quality of vision depends on the intensity of the ambient light*
- *explain that the ear is sensitive to a range of frequencies and intensities of sound*
- *compare sound intensities in W m^{-2} and in decibels*

LEARNING SUMMARY

Lenses and the eye

AQA A 5

When light leaves a lamp or other source of light it spreads out or diverges, reducing in intensity with increasing distance from the source. A **concave** or **diverging lens** exaggerates this effect, making the light more divergent. A **convex** or **converging lens** acts against this effect, so that the light either converges or becomes less divergent.

The diagrams show the effect of these lenses on a parallel beam of light.

Light from a source converges after passing through a convex lens if the source is at a greater distance from the lens than the focal length.

The dotted lines in the diagram of a concave lens show where light **appears** to have come from.

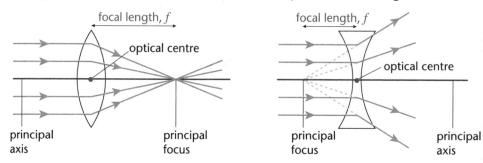

The diagrams also show some important features of the lenses:

- the **optical centre** is at the centre of the lens
- the **principal axis** is a line drawn through the optical centre, perpendicular to the plane of the lens
- the **principal focus** is the image position for light that is initially parallel to the principal axis
- the **focal length** is the distance between the optical centre and the principal focus.

The image is virtual in the case of a concave lens, and real for a convex lens.

The shorter the focal length of a lens, the greater the effect on converging or diverging light that passes through it. This effect is measured by the power of the lens.

Lens power is calculated using the relationship:

power = 1/focal length

The unit of power is the dioptre (D) when the focal length is measured in m.

A virtual image (such as in a plane mirror) can be seen by the eye but cannot be projected onto a screen.

The diagram below shows ray diagrams for an object placed at a distance of 8 cm from converging and diverging lenses each of focal length, f = 5 cm.

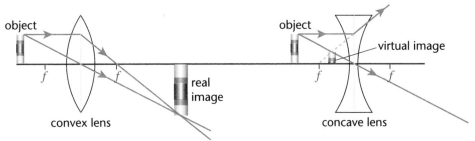

A real image is formed if the light converges after passing through the lens. If the light is still diverging, then the image is virtual.

The position, nature and size of the images can be determined from the diagrams. They can also be calculated using the **lens formula**:

The magnification, i.e. the size of the image compared to the object, is equal to v/u.

The lens formula applies to both convex and concave lenses. It relates the positions of the object and image to the focal length of the lens.

$$\frac{1}{u} + \frac{1}{v} = \frac{1}{f}$$

Where u is the distance between the object and the lens, v is the distance between the image and the lens, and f is the focal length of the lens.

This is known as the 'real is positive' sign convention.

When using the lens formula:

• real objects, images and the focal length of a convex lens have positive values
• virtual images, and the focal length of a concave lens, have negative values.

The eye uses two converging lenses, the cornea and the eye lens, to produce a real image on the retina.

Adjustment of the eye to focus on objects at different distances is called **accommodation**; this is achieved by changing the shape of the lens.

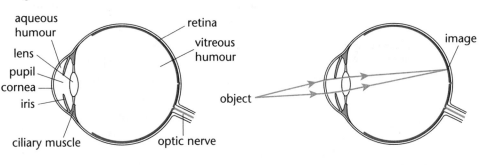

Defective vision

AQA A 5

The common defects in vision are:

• **short sight** or **myopia** when an eye cannot focus on distant objects but can focus on near objects. It is caused by the eyeball being too long or the lens, at its weakest, being too strong.

• **long sight** or **hypermetropia** is the opposite of short sight; distant objects can be seen clearly but near ones cannot. It is caused by the eyeball being too short or the lens, at its strongest, being too weak.

> An eye lens is elastic tissue which becomes more difficult to stretch with increased use.

- **presbyopia** is the condition of being both long-sighted and short-sighted. It often occurs in older people due to the lens becoming stiffer with age.
- **astigmatism** is caused by the surface of the cornea not being spherical. This results in objects in one direction being sharp and in focus while those in a different direction are blurred.

The diagrams show the conditions of short sight and long sight and their correction with converging and diverging lenses respectively.

> These diagrams show light from a distant object arriving at a short-sighted eye.

> These diagrams show light from a near object arriving at a long-sighted eye.

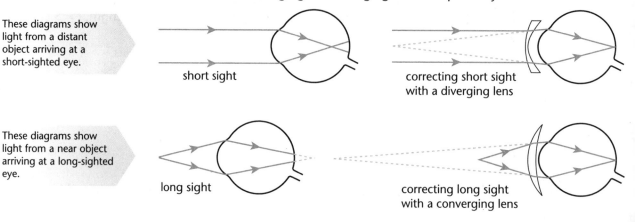

short sight

correcting short sight with a diverging lens

long sight

correcting long sight with a converging lens

The lens formula can be used to calculate the focal length, and hence power, of the correcting lens needed. The object distance, u, is the distance of the actual object and the image distance, v, is the desired distance for the eye to focus on it.

People who suffer from presbyopia often wear bifocal spectacles. The lower half of each lens is convex for reading and the upper half is concave for distant viewing.

To correct astigmatism cylindrical lenses are used. These are less curved in one direction to compensate for the unsymmetrical curvature of the cornea.

Colour vision

AQA A ▸ 5

The light-sensitive cells that make up the retina have different sensitivities:

- **rods** are sensitive to light of different intensities but not of different wavelengths
- there are three types of **cones**, called red, green and blue. Each of these responds to a different range of wavelengths and frequencies.

> This explains why, in low-intensity light such as moonlight, we see in monochrome.

Cones enable **colour vision** but they do not respond to low-intensity light. The graph shows the relative sensitivities of the three types of cone.

> The diagram shows why blue-coloured lamps always appear dim and yellow-coloured lamps appear bright.

The low sensitivity of the blue cones explains why we never perceive this colour as bright as red or yellow. An advertising hoarding designed to catch the eye would not use blue to do so. However, it is a more acceptable colour for 'low-key' signs and buildings.

Vision in low-intensity light is **scotopic** – we cannot detect colour but only differences in brightness. In scotopic vision the cones are not responsive so the rods are the only detectors operating.

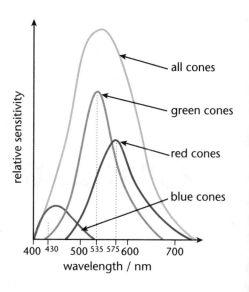

In more intense light the cones take over and vision is **photopic**. Photopic vision allows differentiation of colour in addition to intensity. The ability of the eye to distinguish between two objects that are close together, called its **spatial resolution**, is also greater in photopic vision. Spatial resolution requires at least one unstimulated cell between those that are stimulated. Resolution is greatest at the centre of the retina where the cells are most concentrated. It is worst at the edge of the retina where the cells are more widespread and several rods share a single nerve fibre, so the brain cannot distinguish between individual rods.

> Vision is most acute at the fovea, or yellow spot. This is the point on the retina where the light-sensitive cells are most closely-packed.

The ear and hearing

AQA A ▶ 5

The ear responds to a range of frequencies and a range of intensities.

> **KEY POINT**
>
> The intensity of a wave is defined as the power incident per unit area perpendicular to the direction of wave travel.
>
> $$I = P/A$$
>
> where intensity, I is measured in W m^{-2}. Sound level is measured in **decibels** (dB), and sound level gives a better, if still rather crude and simple, measure of what we actually hear.

> The threshold of hearing is the minimum intensity required to be able to detect a sound.

intensity in W m^{-2}

| 10^{-12} | 10^{-11} | 10^{-10} | 10^{-9} | 10^{-8} | 10^{-7} | 10^{-6} | 10^{-5} | 10^{-4} | 10^{-3} | 10^{-2} | 10^{-1} | 10^{0} | 10^{1} | 10^{2} |

| 0 | 10 | 20 | 30 | 40 | 50 | 60 | 70 | 80 | 90 | 100 | 110 | 120 | 130 | 140 |

sound level in decibels

The correspondence of sound intensity to the decibel scale at a frequency of 1 kHz

> On a logarithmic scale, equal distances on the scale are used to represent multiplication by 10.

A logarithmic scale is used on the diagram because of the way in which the ear responds to relative changes in intensity. It has a **logarithmic response**. This means that equal factor changes in intensity (e.g. ×100) produce equal simple addition changes in perceived sound level (e.g. +20). This leads to the decibel scale for measuring sound level.

> sound level in decibels = $10 \log (I/I_0)$
>
> where I_0, the threshold of hearing, is taken to be 1.0×10^{-12} W m^{-2}.

> Normal conversation has an intensity of about 1×10^{-6} W m^{-2} or 60 dB.

On the decibel scale, an increase of 10 dB corresponds to the intensity becoming ten times as great.

A sound of intensity 120 dB or 1 W m^{-2} causes discomfort; one of 140 dB or 100 W m^{-2} causes extreme pain in the ear.

> By definition, loudness corresponds exactly with the decibel scale of sound level at 1 kHz.

Because our ears are most sensitive to frequencies around 3000 Hz, higher and lower frequencies need a greater intensity to sound equally loud. A more sophisticated method of measuring actual perceived loudness is in phons, where 1 phon is equivalent to a sound level of 1dB at a frequency of 1kHz. The graph shows the variation in intensity required to cause equal loudness at four loudness levels.

This graph shows that:

- the frequency range of a human ear is approximately 20 Hz to 20 000 Hz, but the upper limit falls with increasing age and exposure to noise due to wear of the ossicles (bones that transmit sound through the middle ear) and damage to the sensing hair cells in the inner ear
- the minimum intensity required to detect a sound, I_0, depends on frequency
- the ear is at its most sensitive at frequencies around 3000 Hz.

Progress check

1 An object of height 2.0 cm is placed on the principal axis at a distance of 12.0 cm from a convex lens of focal length 5.0 cm.
By drawing or calculation, work out the position, size and nature of the image.

2 Which **two** parts of the eye converge light as it passes through them?

3 Explain why the brain does not perceive colour in low-intensity ambient light.

4 State **two** factors that reduce the upper limit of the hearing range.

5 A sound has an intensity of 5.0×10^{-7} W m^{-2}. Calculate the sound level in dB.

5 57 dB.
4 Age and exposure to noise.
3 The cones do not function in low-intensity light, and the rods only detect brightness.
2 The cornea and the eye lens.
1 The image is real, 8.6 cm on the other side of the lens and 1.4 cm high.

4.2 Medical and geophysical imaging

After studying this section you should be able to:

- *describe and compare the techniques used for imaging the body*
- *recall the methods used to calculate absorption of harmful radiation*
- *describe processes of imaging the Earth*

The heart and ECG

AQA A   5

The valves are necessary to ensure that blood does not flow from the ventricle to the atrium when the ventricle contracts.

The **heart** is a pump controlled by electrical signals. One side takes in de-oxygenated blood from the body and pumps it to the lungs; the other side takes in oxygenated blood from the lungs and pumps it to the body. The diagram shows the heart and the one-way valves that only allow blood to flow in the directions shown by the arrows, from the **atrium** to the **ventricle**.

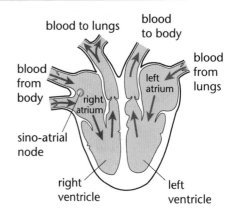

Electrical signals that control the action of the heart:

- are produced in the **sino-atrial node**

- are carried by nerve fibres

- cause contraction of the atria, followed by contraction of the ventricles to pump blood through the heart and round the body.

Body fluids also conduct the electrical signals, enabling them to be detected at the surface of the skin by electrodes. A display, such as that produced on a CRO of the change in voltage with time, is called an **electrocardiagram** (**ECG**).

In the ECG shown in the diagram:

- the pulse at P causes the atria to contract

The pulse that causes relaxation of the atria occurs at the same time as, and is masked by, the QRS pulse.

- the QRS pulses causes the ventricles to contract

- the T pulse causes the ventricles to relax.

Using ultrasound

AQA A   5   OCR A   G485
AQA B   4   WJEC   5

Ultrasound consists of compression waves with a frequency above that of human hearing. It is useful for examining the internal structure of the body because it passes through flesh, but some reflection takes place at tissue boundaries. These reflections are used to generate images.

Pulses of ultrasound are produced and detected by a **piezoelectric crystal**:

The alternating voltages due to the reflected waves are interpreted by a computer to produce an image.

- an alternating voltage applied to the crystal causes it to vibrate

- the voltage is removed to allow the crystal to detect any reflections

- when the crystal is made to vibrate by the reflected pulses it generates an alternating voltage.

The scanning of a fetus is now a routine procedure carried out on all pregnant women to check for abnormalities and determine the precise date when birth is due to take place.

Types of ultrasound images include:

- an **A-scan** (amplitude modulated) which uses the echoes to show how the tissue boundaries are related to depth below the surface of the skin, A-scans are used to make precise determinations of the position of an object such as a brain tumour

- a **B-scan** (brightness modulated) which gives a two-dimensional picture, such as that of a fetus.

Ultrasound scans have the advantage in that ultrasound is non-invasive and does not cause ionisation and damage to body tissue.

Acoustic impedance and reflections

AQA A   5   OCR A   G485

The decrease in intensity of a wave as it travels through a material is known as **attenuation**. Attenuation is due to a number of factors, including:

- the energy of the wave becoming spread over a wider area as it travels from its source

- interactions with the material including absorption, diffraction and scattering.

Sound travels faster in solids than in liquids and faster in liquids than in gases.

The opposition of a material to sound passing through it is called **acoustic impedance**. The acoustic impedance depends on the density of the material and the speed at which sound travels in it. Maximising the transfer of sound from one material to another depends on matching the impedances as closely as possible.

The acoustic impedance, Z, of a material depends on its density, ρ, and the speed of sound within it, c.

$$Z = \rho c$$

It is an important quantity in ultrasound technology because the proportion of sound energy reflected from a boundary depends on the acoustic impedances of the two materials.

The greater the difference in acoustic impedance, the more intense the reflection. For this reason a jelly-like substance is spread over the patient's skin during scanning, so that there is no air between probe and skin. The difference in acoustic impedance of skin and air is large, but that between the jelly and skin is small so it improves the impedance matching and maximises the amount of energy transmitted into the body.

High frequencies of ultra sound needed for good resolution are attenuated more than lower frequencies, so they can only produce high-resolution scans close to the surface of the body.

$$\frac{\text{reflected intensity}}{\text{incident intensity}} = \frac{(Z_2 - Z_1)^2}{(Z_2 + Z_1)^2}$$

where Z_2 is the acoustic impedance of the second material and Z_1 is that of the first.

Note that when $Z_1 = Z_2$ the formula predicts zero reflection.

Producing X-rays

AQA A   5   OCR A   G485
AQA B   4   WJEC   5

X-rays are produced when high-speed electrons hit a target. In the X-ray tube shown in the diagram:

- electrons are emitted from the cathode by thermionic emission

- they are accelerated through the vacuum by the high-voltage anode

A rotating anode X-ray tube

X-rays are emitted when electrons strike the screen of a television or cathode ray tube.

- when they strike the anode about 1% of the energy is transferred to X-rays, the rest heats the anode

- the anode rotates to avoid overheating of one small area.

The **intensity** of the beam is determined by the filament current which causes thermionic emission. The energy of the X-ray photons is determined by the anode voltage; increasing this voltage produces higher-energy, shorter-wavelength X-rays which are more penetrative.

Using X-rays in diagnosis

AQA B   4
OCR A   G485
WJEC   5

Whereas ultrasound images are produced from reflections, X-ray images rely on some absorption and some transmission by the body. As an X-ray beam passes through tissue it becomes attenuated. The intensity of a parallel beam varies exponentially with thickness.

In exponential attenuation, the intensity of the beam is reduced by the same proportion in passing through equal thicknesses of material. This means that the half-value thickness is independent of the initial intensity of the beam.

> **KEY POINT**
>
> The intensity of an X-ray beam, I, after passing through a distance x of absorbing material, is given by:
>
> $$I = I_0 e^{-\mu x}$$
>
> Where I_0 is the initial intensity and μ is a constant, called the **linear attenuation coefficient**. The value of μ depends on the material and the energy of the X-rays.
>
> The **half-value thickness** of a material, $x_{\frac{1}{2}}$, is the thickness that halves the original intensity of the beam. This relationship between μ and $x_{\frac{1}{2}}$ is:
>
> $$\mu x_{\frac{1}{2}} = \ln 2$$

The linear attenuation coefficient changes with changing density, ρ, of the material. The mass attenuation coefficient, μ_m, defined as $\frac{\mu}{\rho}$, is independent of density.

An X-ray photograph is a shadow picture. A detector placed behind the part of the body being X-rayed shows areas of varying greyness, with the dark areas representing the least attenuation of the beam. When bones and teeth are X-rayed, they show up as white. Suitable detectors are:

- black and white photographic film, but this requires a beam of high intensity

- an **intensifying screen** which contains a material that absorbs energy from the X-rays and re-emits it as light, a process known as **fluorescence**. The light then produces a photographic image. Film is more sensitive to light than to X-rays, so less exposure is required.

Studying a moving picture enables medical staff to diagnose faults in the way that organs act or bones move.

- a fluoroscopic image intensifier; the X-rays cause electrons to be ejected from a photocathode. These electrons are then accelerated in the same way as in a cathode ray tube, where they produce a bright image on a fluorescent screen. This technique is used when a 'moving' picture is required.

When intestines are X-rayed, there is very little absorption by the soft tissue and the result is a low-contrast image. The contrast between the intestines and surrounding tissue is increased by giving the patient a 'barium meal'. This lines the intestines with a material that is opaque to X-rays, so they show up as white.

A CT or CAT (**computerised axial tomography**) scan uses a rotating X-ray beam to produce an image of a slice through the body. The beam is rotated around the patient as the patient moves through the beam. The scattered X-rays are detected and used by a computer to build up a picture. Three-dimensional images can be created from images of the individual slices. CAT scans detect slight changes in attenuation and are often used for detecting tumours and cancers.

Fibre optics

| AQA A | 5 |
| AQA B | 4 |

Fibres are normally clad with a glass of lower refractive index than the core in order to minimise the value of the critical angle.

An **optical fibre** can transmit light round corners using **total internal reflection**. When light strikes the interface between the fibre core and its cladding it is reflected back inside the fibre provided that the angle of incidence is greater than the critical angle. This is shown in the diagram.

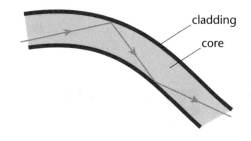
cladding
core

An **endoscope** is a bundle of fibres that can be used for viewing inside the body or performing surgery.

For viewing inside the body two sets of fibres are used:

- the fibres that take light into the body are **non-coherent**, they do not need to stay in the same position relative to other fibres
- the fibres that transmit the image out of the body are **coherent**, they are in the same positions relative to each other at each end of the bundle. The narrower the fibres used, the greater the resolution of the image.

Tissue becomes heated by absorption of the energy from laser radiation.

Lasers are sources of high-intensity electromagnetic radiation that can be passed into the body along an optical fibre. This allows heating to be applied to small areas of tissue by absorption of the laser beam. Used in this way optical fibres can:

- act as a scalpel by cutting through tissue but without causing bleeding
- repair tears and stop bleeding by coagulating body fluids.

Magnetic resonance imaging

| AQA A | 5 | OCR A | G485 |
| AQA B | 4 | WJEC | 5 |

Very powerful electromagnets are needed to produce the magnetic fields required by an MRI scanner.

Magnetic resonance imaging (MRI) detects the presence of hydrogen nuclei. Since body tissue has a high water content, it can be used to produce an image of the body. It works by applying pulses of a high-intensity and high-frequency magnetic field which results in the emission of electromagnetic radiation from the nuclei by the following process.

- Hydrogen nuclei spin, giving them a magnetic field.
- When an external magnetic field is applied, they rotate around the direction of the field. This rotation is called **precession**, it is like that of a spinning top when it 'wobbles'.
- The frequency of precession is called the **Larmor frequency**.
- Application of a pulse of radiation at the Larmor frequency causes **resonance**, the nuclei absorb the energy into the precession.
- When the pulse is removed the nuclei lose the energy, emitting it as electromagnetic radiation. This takes place over a short period of time known as the **relaxation time**.

The emissions from the hydrogen nuclei are detected by a radio aerial and processed by a computer to give three-dimensional body imaging. MRI scanning is non-invasive and does not cause ionisation, but it is very expensive in terms of the capital equipment and running costs.

PET scans

AQA A   5
OCR A   G485
WJEC   5

PET scans, like MRI and CAT scans, produce images of the inside of the body. PET stands for positron emission tomography. By injection or drink, a β^+ emitting isotope is introduced to the body.

The isotopes emit positrons (β^+) which meet electrons in the surrounding material, resulting in mutual annihilation and emission of gamma radiation which can be deflected from outside the body to allow an image to be produced.

The radioisotopes can be chemically bonded to substances such as glucose, so that parts of the body where glucose is dense show up brightly on the image.

Using ionising radiation

OCR A   2
WJEC   5

Hydrogen peroxide is extremely corrosive and can cause extensive damage when formed within a cell.

Ionising radiation such as X-rays and gamma rays:

- can damage enzymes and DNA by ionisation
- can cause the formation of hydrogen peroxide from water, which in turn causes cell damage.

The effects of this include skin burns, cancer and sterility. For this reason, **exposure** to ionising radiation should always be kept to a minimum.

> **KEY POINT**
>
> Exposure, X, is defined in terms of the ionisation that the radiation causes:
> $$X = \frac{q}{m}$$
> where q is the total charge of one sign of ion (either positive or negative) produced in a mass m of air. Exposure is measured in C kg^{-1}.

The **absorbed dose** of radiation measures the energy absorbed by a material.

> **KEY POINT**
>
> Absorbed dose, D, is defined as
> $$D = \frac{E}{m}$$
> where E is the energy absorbed by mass m. Its unit is the gray (Gy) where 1 Gy = 1 J kg^{-1}.

The effect of absorbing radiation depends on the absorbed dose and the type of radiation involved. Alpha particles and neutrons are absorbed over a short distance whereas X-rays and gamma rays cause less damage for the same absorbed dose as their energy is distributed over a greater mass of material. The **quality factor** takes into account the effects of different radiations and is used to calculate equivalent effects of absorbing different radiations.

Effectively the dose equivalent is used to compare the energies absorbed by doses of different radiations.

> **KEY POINT**
>
> The **dose equivalent**, H, of a radiation is defined by:
> $$H = Q \times D$$
> where Q is the quality factor of the radiation.
> Dose equivalent is measured in sievert (Sv).

X-rays and gamma rays have a quality factor of 1, while that for radiation which is absorbed more readily is higher, that for alpha particles being 20.

The effects of a dose of ionising radiation can be classified as stochastic (random) or non-stochastic:

- stochastic effects such as cancer are due to cell mutations; no minimum dose is required but the greater the dose the more likely it is that the effect will occur

- non-stochastic effects such as skin burns need a minimum dose to occur; the greater the dose above this minimum value, the worse the effect.

When X-rays and gamma rays are used to kill a malignant tumour several beams are used, aimed at the patient in different directions. The diagram shows how the beams intersect at the tumour. This ensures that the tumour receives a high dose while that in the surrounding tissue is relatively low.

A similar effect is achieved by rotating a single beam around the patient so that the beam is always directed towards the tumour.

this area receives the greatest intensity of radiation

Imaging the Earth's surface

AQA B   4

Satellites can use different parts of the electromagnetic spectrum to image the surface of the Earth. They can use 'radar' processes, in which the satellite emits radiation and detects the reflections. They can use reflected sunlight. They can use emitted infrared radiation. A satellite might scan the Earth and measure different intensities of infrared radiation, for example. The data can be presented as a map, using different colours to represent different intensities. Since these colours are not the natural colours of the surface, such an image is called a false-colour image.

False colours can also be used to represent gravitational anomalies, which are patterns of varying gravitational field strength due, for example, to different densities of rock. A satellite's height varies very slightly as is passes over different areas, and the variation is enough to be measured to produce gravitational anomaly maps of the whole of the Earth.

Seismic surveys

AQA B   4

Seismic surveys use reflected waves created by earthquakes or deliberate explosions to build up images of the Earth's crust, often vertical cross-sections of the ground. The principles are similar to those of sonar in water or ultrasound in the human body.

Surveying the ground

AQA B   4

Resistivity surveys are useful in fields such as pollution monitoring and archaeology. Resistivity, ρ, is a property of material, related to the resistance of a given cross sectional area normal to the current and the length of material.

$$\rho = RA \, / \, l$$

Two probes stuck in to the ground, with a potential difference applied to them, can be used to measure the resistance of the ground, and the distance between them (l) and the effective cross sectional area through which the current flows can be used to determine the resistivity of the ground material.

The presence of former human habitation, evidenced by regular patterns of varying resistivity due to the presence of old timber or charcoal in the ground, or to different water-holding properties of different material, can be detected. So also can more recent polluting materials.

There are subtle local variations in magnetic field for similar reasons. A proton magnetometer is a sensitive instrument that measures magnetic field by detecting the resonant frequency of oscillating (or 'precessing') the hydrogen nuclei (protons), and this frequency is highly dependent on the local magnetic field. (The principle is related to that of MRI imaging.)

Metal detectors transmit radio waves to detect buried (or other) metal objects. the radio waves induce e.m.f.s in metal objects, which then also act as transmitters. The metal detector has a receiver to detect these responses to its own signals.

Progress check

1 In an X-ray tube:
   a what determines the intensity of the X-ray beam
   b what determines the wavelength of the X-rays produced?

2 Suggest **two** reasons why non-invasive examination is preferred to invasive examination.

3 Why is ultrasound preferred to X-rays for producing an image of a fetus?

3 Ultrasound does not cause ionisation or damage body tissue.

The patient recovers more rapidly.
2 There are no wounds, so infections cannot occur.

 b The anode voltage.
1 a The current in the filament.

4.3 Starlight

After studying this section you should be able to:

- describe the structure of reflecting, refracting and radio telescopes
- explain how the resolution of a telescope depends on its aperture
- recall that a charge-coupled device is used to give a brighter image
- explain how the evolution of a star depends on its mass
- compare the apparent magnitudes and calculate absolute magnitudes of stars
- describe how stars are classified in terms of their brightness, temperature and composition
- explain how an absorption spectrum gives information about the elements present in a star

LEARNING SUMMARY

Optical telescopes

AQA A   5

A **refracting telescope** uses two converging lenses. The objective lens produces a real image at its principal focus. The weaker this lens, the greater the size of the image produced and the longer the telescope. The eyepiece lens acts as a magnifying glass; by placing it so that its principal focus is at the position of the real image being magnified, the final image is formed 'at infinity' and the telescope is said to be in **normal adjustment**. This is shown in the diagram.

> Refracting telescopes are limited in the diameter of the objective lens that can be used, since the weight of a large lens can cause the glass to flow and change its shape.

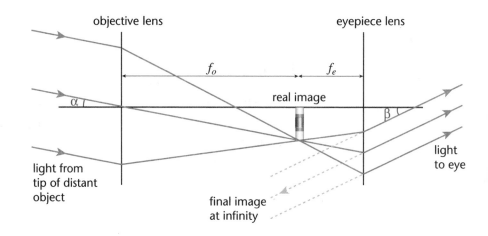

Since the size of the image on the retina depends on the angle subtended by the light reaching the eye, **angular magnification** is used to measure the factor by which the telescope increases this angle.

> **KEY POINT**
>
> Angular magnification, M, $= \dfrac{\text{angle subtended at eye by image}}{\text{angle subtended at eye by object}} = \dfrac{\beta}{\alpha}$
>
> For a telescope in normal adjustment, $M = \dfrac{f_o}{f_e}$

> As with a converging lens, the principal focus is the point where light parallel to the principal axis converges.

In the Cassegrain **reflecting telescope** a concave mirror is used to converge parallel light from a distant object. This would produce a real image at its principal focus, but the light is intercepted by a small convex mirror which produces an enlarged image for magnification by the eyepiece lens. This is shown in the diagram.

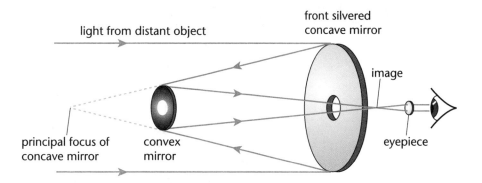

light from distant object

front silvered concave mirror

image

principal focus of concave mirror

convex mirror

eyepiece

Both types of telescope can produce blurring of the image called **aberration**.

- **Chromatic aberration** is due to light of different wavelengths being focused at different points; it is reduced by using combination lenses made with two different types of glass.

- **Spherical aberration** is caused by light that strikes the outer edges of a lens or mirror being brought to a focus slightly closer than those from the centre; it is reduced by using plano-convex lenses (only one face is curved) in refracting telescopes and parabolic mirrors in reflecting telescopes.

Resolution

AQA A ▷ S

The **resolving power** of a telescope describes its ability to distinguish two stars that are close together, rather than identify them as a single star. When light passes through a circular aperture it is diffracted. The bright central ring (known as the **Airy disc**) is surrounded by a number of low-intensity rings. The diagram shows the variation of intensity with angle from the centre of the Airy disc.

intensity / f

θ

This is the separation required for both Airey discs to be discernible.

To be able to distinguish between two stars:

- the minimum separation of the images is when the central maximum of each is at the same place as the first minimum of the other

The symbol ≈ means approximately rather than precisely equal to.

- the **Rayleigh criterion** for this to happen is that the angle between the stars $\theta \approx \dfrac{\lambda}{D}$, where D is the diameter of the telescope and θ is in radians

- θ is known as the **resolving power** of the telescope.

CCDs

AQA A ▷ S

'Digital' images can be produced using **charge-coupled devices**.

- A charge-coupled device is a thin slice of silicon whose upper surface is divided into a large number of pixels

- When a photon of light is absorbed by a pixel, the energy releases an electron from the silicon onto the pixel.

This means that the probability of an individual photon liberating an electron is 0.7.

- The charge on any pixel is proportional to the number of photons absorbed.

Information from each pixel is read and interpreted by a computer. The charge-coupled device has a much higher quantum efficiency than photographic film, at more than 70% compared to 4%.

Stars are black bodies

AQA A   5

All objects emit electromagnetic radiation over a range of wavelengths that depends on the temperature of the object. Increasing the temperature of an object results in:

- an increase in the power radiated
- the wavelength at which the maximum power is radiated becoming shorter.

A **black body** absorbs all wavelengths of electromagnetic radiation and reflects none. However, it need not appear black, as solid objects at a temperature greater than about 600°C emit visible radiation. The rate of emission of radiation from a black body at different temperatures is shown in the graph opposite.

> The area between the graph line and the wavelength axis represents the total power radiated. The graph shows that this increases with increasing temperature.

The dotted line shows how the wavelength at which the maximum power is emitted depends on the temperature of the black body. Knowledge of this wavelength enables the surface temperature of a star to be estimated using **Wien's law**.

> Note that the unit 'm K' is 'metre × Kelvin', not milliKelvin, which would be written as mK.

> **KEY POINT**
>
> Wien's law relates the wavelength at which the maximum power is emitted by a black body, λ_{max}, to its temperature:
> $$\lambda_{max}T = 2.90 \times 10^{-3} \text{ m K}$$
> Where T is the temperature of the object in K.

In practice it may be difficult to determine λ precisely because:

- the instrument used to detect the radiation may not have the same sensitivity for all wavelengths
- the atmosphere absorbs some wavelengths of light more than others, so the intensity of these wavelengths may be reduced by more than that of others as the light travels through the atmosphere.

The power radiated by a black body depends on both its surface area and its temperature.

> When applying Stefan's law to stars, it is assumed that stars are black bodies in that they are unselective in the wavelengths of radiation that they emit and absorb.

> **KEY POINT**
>
> **Stefan's law** states that:
> the power radiated per m² of a black body is proportional to its (absolute temperature)⁴
> $$\frac{P}{A} = \sigma T^4$$
> where σ is Stefan's constant and has the value 5.67×10^{-8} W m^{-2} K^{-4}.

When applying Stefan's law:

- the power radiated is calculated from measurements of the intensity of the light received and the distance of the star from the Earth, using the **inverse square law**
- the inverse square law states that the intensity decreases as the inverse of the square of the distance, $I \propto \dfrac{1}{d^2}$

If the temperature of a star is calculated from Wien's law, then Stefan's law can be used to estimate the area needed for the star to have the same power output as the Sun (3.8×10^{26} W). The surface area, and hence the radius of the star, can be calculated by comparing the absolute magnitudes (see page 143).

Spectral classes

AQA A 5

Analysis of the emission and absorption spectra of a star enables it to be classified according to its temperature and composition. The table shows the characteristics of the seven classes of star in order of decreasing surface temperature.

Type	Colour	Surface temp/K × 10³	Absorption of hydrogen Balmer lines	Elements detected in absorption spectrum
O	blue	40	weak	helium ions
B	pale blue	20	fairly strong	helium atoms
A	white	10	strong	hydrogen
F	pale yellow	7	medium	ionised metals such as calcium and iron
G	yellow	6	weak	calcium ions and iron atoms
K	orange	5	weak	calcium and iron atoms, together with some molecules
M	red	3	weak	molecules of metal oxides

Note that observed absorption spectra are produced as light passes through the outer layers of stars. This table shows that:

- in the surface layers, ionised helium is only present in the hottest stars where the temperature is high enough to ionise helium atoms

- stars in groups B and A show strong absorption by hydrogen in the Balmer series; this is the part of the hydrogen emission spectrum due to exciting electrons from the first excited energy level above the ground state. This energy level is given the value n = 2, where n = 1 corresponds to the ground state. Absorption of these spectral lines shows that the temperature is cool enough for hydrogen atoms to exist but hot enough for them to be in an excited state

- the relatively cool stars in classes F and G show absorption lines due to ionised metals

- stars in classes K and M are cool enough for molecules such as those of metal oxides to exist without being separated into atoms or ionised.

Analysing an absorption spectrum obtained at the Earth's surface can be misleading, as the following diagram shows.

This graph shows the reduction in intensity of all wavelengths as the radiation passes through the atmosphere, with particular wavelengths being absorbed more than others. Information from spectra obtained from satellites gives a fuller picture than that from spectra obtained at ground level.

Quasars

AQA A   5

Quasars are the most distant objects that can be detected. They are very bright objects which were first discovered by detection of the radio signals that some of them emit. Analysis of the light from a quasar reveals that:

- the spectrum is an emission spectrum, with very bright lines superimposed on a continuous spectrum
- these lines show enormous red-shift, indicating that quasars are moving with very high speeds.

Analysis of the red-shift indicates that some quasars are moving at speeds greater than 90% of the speed of light at distances of more than ten billion (1×10^{10}) light years. They are relatively small and yet they appear to emit thousands of times as much energy as a typical galaxy.

However, this may be misleading. If some other mechanism is responsible for the red-shift, they could turn out to be much closer and less bright than was at first believed.

The life of a star

AQA A   5   Edexcel context   5
Edexcel concept   5

When protons fuse together the resulting nucleus has less mass than its constituent particles. Einstein's equation $E = mc^2$ is used to calculate the energy released in fusion.

When a star is formed:

- clouds containing dust, hydrogen and helium collapse due to gravitational forces
- the contraction causes heating
- the temperature in the core becomes hot enough for fusion reactions to occur
- energy is released as hydrogen nuclei fuse, eventually forming the nuclei of helium.

The star is now in its **main sequence**. How long it remains like this depends on its mass; the more massive the star, the shorter the main sequence.

When there is no longer sufficient hydrogen in the core of a star to maintain its energy production and brightness the star cools:

Fusion to form nuclei more massive than iron requires energy to be supplied, so energy cannot be released by further fusion reactions when the core consists of iron.

- the core contracts but the outer layers expand, forming a **red giant** or **red supergiant**, depending on its size
- increased heating of the core creates temperatures hot enough for the helium nuclei to fuse, forming carbon and oxygen.

In a small star like our Sun, once the helium has fused the core contracts to form a **white dwarf**, and the outer layers are ejected. The star then cools to an invisible **black dwarf**.

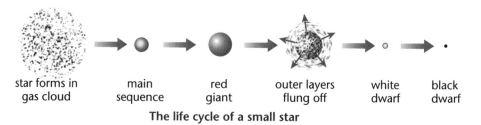

| star forms in gas cloud | main sequence | red giant | outer layers flung off | white dwarf | black dwarf |

The life cycle of a small star

In a larger star:

- further fusion reactions occur and the star becomes a **blue supergiant**
- the nuclei of more massive elements are formed until the core is mainly iron, the most stable element
- the core now collapses and the heating causes the star to increase in brightness, it is a **supernova**, an exploding star

- in the explosion the outer layers are flung off to form a new dust cloud and the dense core remains as a **neutron star** or, in the case of a very massive star, a **black hole**, whose gravitational field is so strong that light cannot escape from it.

The boundary around a black hole, beyond which nothing can be seen, is called the **event horizon**. Its size is related to the mass of the black hole.

The Schwarzschild radius

AQA A ▶ 5

> The **Schwarzschild radius**, R_s is the radius of the event horizon around a black hole:
>
> $$R_s = \frac{2GM}{c^2}$$
>
> where M is the mass of the black hole, G is the universal gravitational constant and c is the speed of light.

KEY POINT

Star magnitudes

AQA A ▶ 5

The brightness of the light received from a star, known as its **apparent magnitude**, depends on both its actual brightness and its distance from the Earth. A star of magnitude 1 is defined as appearing 100 times as bright as a star of magnitude 6, so one unit on the magnitude scale corresponds to a change in brightness by a factor of 2.5.

The magnitude scale is a logarithmic scale, equal changes on this scale correspond to the brightness changing by the same factor.

> The apparent magnitude, m, of a star is related to intensity of its observed radiation, I, by the expression:
> $$m = -2.5 \log_{10} I + \text{constant}$$

KEY POINT

When the equation is used to compare apparent magnitudes, the constant has no significance as it does not appear in the relationship $m_1 - m_2$, the difference in the apparent magnitudes of two stars.

Apparent magnitudes are compared by the intensities of the images on photographic film or other detector exposed for a fixed time.

The smaller the apparent magnitude of a star, the brighter it appears to be. The brightest star seen from the Earth is the Sun, with an apparent magnitude of –27.

To compare the actual brightnesses with which stars blaze, the intensities they emit rather than the brightness we see from Earth, the effect of distance on the detected brightness needs to be taken into account. One system for doing this comparison is based on the magnitudes that stars would have if they were the same distance from the Earth.

> The **absolute magnitude**, M, of a star is the apparent magnitude it would have if it were a distance of 10 pc from the Earth.
>
> It is calculated from the apparent magnitude using the expression
> $$m - M = 5 \log (d) - 5$$
> where d is the distance of the star from the Earth in pc.

KEY POINT

When the absolute magnitudes of stars are plotted against their surface temperatures, the result is a **Hertzsprung–Russell** diagram.

The H-R diagram shows that:

- different types of star occupy specific regions on the diagram
- most stars are in the main sequence band, with the more massive stars in the upper left corner
- the white dwarfs are hot but dim because of their small size.

Note that, on the diagram, movement towards the right corresponds to decreasing temperature.

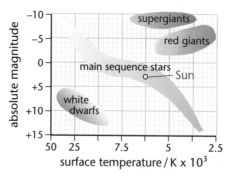

Progress check

1 What is the advantage of a reflecting optical telescope over a refracting one?

2 A radio telescope has a dish diameter of 75 m. What is its resolving power when detecting 0.50 m wavelength radio waves?

3 The second nearest star to Earth subtends an angle of 1.52 arc seconds when measured from opposite extremes of the Earth's orbit. Calculate its distance from the Earth in pc.

4 What causes the release of energy from a star in its main sequence?

5 What is meant by an *event horizon*?

6 The apparent magnitude of Venus is –4, and that of the Sun is –27. By what factor does the Sun appear brighter than Venus?

7 Suggest why the magnitudes of red giants are greater than some main sequence stars that have a higher surface temperature.

8 Explain why dark lines in an absorption spectrum correspond to bright lines in the emission spectrum of the same element.

8 A gaseous element can only emit and absorb certain frequencies or wavelengths. These frequencies or wavelengths are the same for emission and absorption. When white light passes through the gas it absorbs the frequencies in its emission spectrum, leaving dark lines.

7 The red giants have a much greater surface area.

6 1.4×10^9

5 The boundary around a black hole, beyond which nothing can be seen.

4 The fusion of protons into more massive nuclei, eventually forming helium.

3 1.32 pc.

2 6.7×10^{-3} radians

1 It can be made of much larger diameter, allowing increased resolution and brighter images.

4.4 The expanding Universe

After studying this section you should be able to:

- *describe how the work of Copernicus, Kepler and Galileo enabled greater understanding of the Solar System and the Universe*
- *explain how line spectra give evidence for the composition of stars*
- *describe how Doppler shift can be used to measure the speed of a star relative to the Earth*
- *explain how Hubble's law can be used to estimate the age of the Universe*

LEARNING SUMMARY

Stars and galaxies

AQA A	5	OCR A	G485
Edexcel concept	5	OCR B	G494
Edexcel context	5	WJEC	4

The Sun is a small star situated on one arm close to the outer edge of a spiral galaxy called the Milky Way. The photos show the three shapes of galaxy: spiral, elliptical and irregular.

The Milky Way Galaxy whirls around at enormous speeds but, like the planets in the Solar System, the orbital time of stars increases with increasing distance from the centre. When Newton's law of gravitation is applied to the movement of the Solar System within the Galaxy, the mass of the planets is ignored as this has only a small effect. The mass of all the other stars in a galaxy cannot be ignored when applying the law to an individual star, but only those within the orbit of a star are taken into account as it is the gravitational attraction of these stars that provides the centripetal force.

> **KEY POINT**
>
> Newton's law applied to the orbit of a star gives the relationship between the orbital time, T, and the orbital radius, r:
>
> $$T^2 = \frac{4\pi^2 r^3}{GM}$$
>
> where M is the total mass contained within the orbit of the star.

Olbers' paradox

OCR A	G485

A paradox is an apparent contradiction.

Newton pictured a static Universe that stretched to infinity, with stars being uniformly distributed throughout. Otherwise, he argued, the Universe would collapse due to the gravitational attraction of its mass. **Olbers' paradox** says that if this were the case the sky should be bright at night. To understand why:

- imagine that the Universe is split into shells of equal thickness, like the structure of an onion
- the intensity of the light received from a star in a shell of radius r is four times that received from a star in a shell of radius 2r
- because it has four times the volume, a shell of radius 2r contains four times as many stars as one of radius r
- it follows that the light from each shell is equally bright, and if there are an infinite number of shells the sky should be bright at night.

The contradiction arises because of the incorrect assumptions that:

The Universe is finite and expanding.

- the Universe is infinite
- the Universe is static.

Early models of the Solar System

OCR A   G485
OCR B   G494
WJEC   5

Copernicus' model of the Solar System (circa 1520), in which he proposed that the Sun and not the Earth is at the centre, provided a much simpler model than previous ones for understanding the apparent backwards motion, at times, of the planets, and their changes in brightness.

Kepler later took the model one stage further (circa 1600) and established that the planets move in elliptical orbits. Kepler's three laws of planetary motion are:

1 planets follow elliptical orbits around the Sun, with the Sun at one focus
2 a line joining a planet to the Sun sweeps out equal areas in equal times
3 $T^2 \propto R^3$, where T is the orbital period of a planet and R is its mean distance from the Sun.

Unlike Copernicus, Galileo did publish his findings. His support for the Copernican model lead to his imprisonment. The last years of his life were spent under house arrest.

In order to avoid conflict with the established teachings of the Church, Copernicus did not publish his ideas until just before his death in 1543. When **Galileo** (circa 1610) observed moons orbiting Jupiter, he realised that this supported the Copernican model and that the Church's teaching that 'everything in the Universe orbits the Earth' had to be wrong.

Having established his laws of motion on Earth, **Newton** applied these to the movement of the planets (circa 1690). This lead to the realisation that for Kepler's second law to be true there had to be a force directed inwards. He described that force in his law of universal gravitation.

> Newton's law of gravitation can be used to show the relationship between the orbital period, T, and radius of orbit, R:
>
> $$T^2 = \left(\frac{4\pi^2}{GM_s}\right) R^3$$
>
> which is in agreement with Kepler's third law.

KEY POINT

Kepler's law was derived by analysing data, so it provides experimental support for Newton's law.

Although Newton's law and Kepler's laws supported each other, the orbit of Uranus did not. Uranus was seen to change orbital speed in a way that Newton's theory did not explain. Not, that is, until the theory was used to predict the existence of Neptune as being responsible for the irregularities in Uranus' orbit. When Neptune was found, in the location predicted, this provided further powerful support for Newton's ideas.

The modern picture

OCR A   G485
OCR B   G494
WJEC   5

The **Solar System** includes:

- the **Sun**, the star at its centre and its source of energy
- the **planets**, which can be seen by reflected sunlight
- planetary **satellites**, the natural satellites are the planets' moons
- **comets**, which unlike the planets can orbit the Sun in any plane and any direction.

The **Universe** includes:

- galaxies; a **galaxy** is a collection of stars, between a few million and hundreds of billions in number, held together by gravitational forces

- an uncountable number of stars
- **microwave radiation**, thought to be left over from the creation of the Universe, and corresponding to a temperature of 3 K.

The cosmological principle

OCR A   G485

The **cosmological principle** is a statement that there is nothing special about the observed physical world we see on Earth. It states that:

- on a large scale, the Universe does not differ in any one direction compared to any other direction
- physical laws and principles apply equally throughout the Universe.

Astronomical distances

AQA A	5	OCR A	G485
Edexcel concept	5	OCR B	G494
Edexcel context	5	WJEC	4

Different units are used to measure distances in our Solar System, our galaxy and beyond our galaxy. The table shows these units and gives their equivalent in m.

Unit	Definition	Equivalent distance in m
astronomical unit (AU)	mean distance between Earth and Sun	1.5×10^{11}
light year	distance travelled by light in 1 year	9.5×10^{15}
parsec (pc)	distance between observations in AU / angle subtended (in arc seconds, where 1 arc second = 1/3600 degrees)	3.1×10^{16}

The AU is used for measuring distances within the Solar System, the light year for close stars and the parsec for more distant stars.

The next table shows typical sizes and masses of the Universe and its contents.

Object	Distance in light years	Mass in kg
nearest star	4.3	10^{30}
Milky Way galaxy	10^5 measured across from opposite extremes	10^{40}
Universe	10^{10} measured across from opposite extremes	unknown, but thought to be around 10^{55}

Emission and absorption spectra

OCR B   G494

Line spectra are emitted when an electric current passes in an ionised gas. Light is emitted when an electron loses energy either by being captured by a gas ion or by a transition to a lower energy level.

A similar effect causes a gas that is hot (typically in excess of 1000°C) to emit light. When this happens:

- electrons gain energy in the collisions due to thermal motion of the particles
- electrons can only absorb the amounts of energy associated with movement to a higher energy level
- electromagnetic radiation is emitted when an electron loses energy and moves to a lower energy level.

The temperature at which a gas starts to emit light depends on the smallest energy level transition that results in the emission of a visible photon.

As each element has its own characteristic **emission spectrum**, the composition of a gaseous object that emits its own light can be determined by analysing this spectrum.

This is how helium was discovered in solar flares, but the spectrum obtained from the body of the Sun and other stars is not a line emission spectrum but a line **absorption spectrum**. It contains the full range of visible wavelengths with a large number of 'black' lines, where wavelengths are missing.

Inside a star the particles are very close together, and their energy levels overlap. So unlike a gas at normal temperatures and pressures on Earth, there are no limits to the energy level transitions that are possible. This explains why a star emits the full frequency range of the visible spectrum. The explanation of the black lines is:

> Hot solids and liquids can emit all wavelengths, and appear white hot, because there are no restrictions on the allowed energy level transitions.

- a gas can only absorb the wavelengths of electromagnetic radiation that it emits, since these correspond to the same energy level transitions in the opposite directions
- when white light from the body of the Sun passes through the cooler, gaseous surface layers, the elements present absorb their own characteristic wavelengths
- this energy is re-emitted in all directions leaving a dark line in the spectrum that reaches the Earth.

The composition of a star is determined from the absorption spectrum and the wavelengths missing from that spectrum, rather than the wavelengths it contains.

Doppler shift

AQA A	5	OCR A	G485
Edexcel concept	5	OCR B	G494
Edexcel context	5	WJEC	4

> Radar systems, used to measure the speed of moving cars, also use the Doppler effect.

You can tell whether an unseen aircraft is moving towards or away from you by the pitch of the engines. You receive higher frequency sounds when it is moving towards you than when it is moving away. This is due to the **Doppler effect**, the difference between the frequency of a wave emitted and that of the wave received when there is relative movement of the wave source and an observer.

> **KEY POINT**
>
> For light, the change in frequency, Δf, or wavelength, $\Delta \lambda$, due to relative motion is given by:
> $$\Delta f/f = \Delta \lambda / \lambda = v/c$$
> where v is the speed of the source relative to the observer and c is the speed of light.

The spectral lines in the absorption spectrum of a star observed from the Earth are subject to Doppler shift:

- a shift towards the blue end of the spectrum corresponds to a reduction in wavelength and an increase in frequency; this happens when a star is moving towards the Earth
- a shift towards the red end of the spectrum corresponds to an increase in wavelength and a reduction in frequency.

Hubble and red-shift

We live in an expanding Universe. Evidence for this comes from the shift in frequency and wavelength of the light received from other galaxies. Light from the relatively nearby Andromeda galaxy is shifted towards the blue end of the spectrum, but for every other galaxy the shift is towards the red. The amount of shift depends on the speed of the galaxy relative to the Earth, known as the speed of recession.

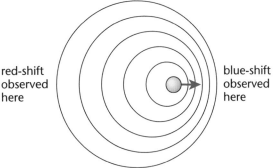

red-shift observed here

blue-shift observed here

How movement of a star causes a difference between the wavelengths emitted and those received

Hubble discovered that:

the speed of recession of a galaxy is proportional to its distance from the Earth.

This is known as **Hubble's law**, and it gives rise to Hubble's constant.

> Hubble's law seems to state that the Earth is the centre of the expansion. This is not the case. Measurements taken from any point in an expanding Universe would give the same pattern.

KEY POINT

Hubble's law can be written as

$$v \propto d \text{ or } v = Hd$$

where v is the speed of a galaxy relative to the Earth, d is its distance from the Earth and H is Hubble's constant.

H has units s^{-1} but its value is not known precisely.

An alternative unit for H is $km\ s^{-1}\ Mpc^{-1}$.

The expansion of the Universe gives evidence to support the **Big Bang** theory. According to this theory:

- the Universe started with an enormous 'explosion' more than 13 thousand million years ago
- initially the Universe was very small and very hot
- the Universe has been cooling as the galaxies have been moving away from each other ever since.

> The energy of the background radiation is equivalent to that radiated from an object at a temperature of about 3 K.

The theory is also supported by the existence of microwave background radiation that fills the whole Universe. This is thought to be electromagnetic radiation left over from the initial 'explosion'. Due to the expansion of the Universe its wavelength has increased and its energy has decreased.

The age of the Universe

Measurements of the value of the Hubble constant enable the age of the Universe to be estimated. This involves measuring both the relative speed and the distance of a star from the Earth. To estimate the distance to a star:

- for close stars (up to 300 light years) the apparent movement, called parallax movement, of the star across the fixed background of more distant stars is used. This involves measuring the position of the star when the Earth is at opposite points in its orbit.

The age of the Universe is estimated from $\frac{1}{H}$.

• for more distant stars observations of the spectrum, brightness and periodic variation in brightness are needed.

Both methods only produce an estimate. In the case of close stars, movement of the star itself and the Sun also affect the apparent change in position due to the Earth's movement. For more distant stars, scattering of light from the star as it passes through the Earth's atmosphere leads to uncertainty in the measurements.

Since the distance of a star, d, cannot be measured very precisely it follows that there is uncertainty about the value of the Hubble constant, H. Probably the only certain thing about it is that it is not constant! Its value is probably decreasing due to galaxies slowing down because of the effect of their gravitational pulls on each other.

The diagram shows how the speed of a galaxy relative to the Earth varies with distance.

gradient of graph = Hubble's constant

Each galaxy contributes a point on the graph. The galaxies do not all lie close to the line so there is significant uncertainty in the value of the gradient.

The Hubble constant can be calculated from any pair of values obtained from the graph. An estimate of the age of the Universe is then obtained by calculating the reciprocal of this constant.

In the beginning

An anti-particle has the same mass as its corresponding particle, but the opposite charge (if any). When they collide they cease to exist, forming gamma rays or other particles.

There is little direct evidence to support any theory about what happened in the first fraction of a second after the 'Big Bang'. The energies of the particles that existed would be so vast that it is impossible at the present time to accelerate particles to these energies in order to study their behaviour.

Before the first 0.01 s:

• electrons and positrons (anti-electrons) and quarks existed

• quarks combined to form nucleons and their anti-particles.

After the first 0.01 s.

• annihilation of nucleons and anti-nucleons occurred, leaving an excess of nucleons

• after about 15 s, electron–positron annihilation left an excess of electrons

• after about 100 s, fusion of protons formed light nuclei such as helium

• after about 5×10^5 years, atoms formed from nuclei and electrons

The formation of neutral atoms resulted in less electrostatic repulsion.

• stars and galaxies began to form as there was less electrostatic repulsion between particles to oppose the gravitational attraction

• after about 5×10^6 years the formation of clusters of galaxies continued to increase the local variations in the density of the Universe.

What about the future?

Edexcel concept   5   OCR A   G485

Edexcel context   5

There are three possibilities for the future of the Universe:

* it will continue to expand
* it will reach a steady size
* it will contract, ending in a '**Big Crunch**'.

Whatever the answer, it depends on the gravitational attraction between the galaxies, and this in turn depends on the average density, known as the **mass–energy density** to emphasise that the energy in the Universe has considerable mass and contributes to its density.

The future of the Universe depends on its density. The **critical density** is that required to hold the Universe in a steady state; if the density is less than this then the Universe will continue to expand. If the density is greater than the critical density, the Universe will stop expanding and contract, resulting in the 'Big Crunch'.

Newton's law of gravitation, together with Hubble's law, can be used to show that:

> A strict derivation of the relationship is only possible using relativity theory.

The critical density, ρ_0, is given by the expression $$\rho_0 = 3H^2/8\pi G$$

KEY POINT

This gives a value of approximately 2.0×10^{-26} kg m^{-3}, depending on the value assumed for Hubble's constant.

The following graphs show the variation in the size of the Universe for the open Universe (infinite expansion) and closed Universe (final contraction) models.

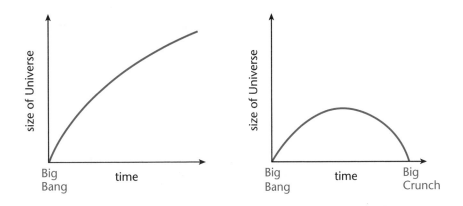

Progress check

1. Explain why dark lines in an absorption spectrum correspond to bright lines in an emission spectrum of the same element.

2. A star is moving away from the Earth at a speed of 1.0×10^6 m s^{-1}.

   Calculate the fractional difference in wavelength, $\Delta\lambda/\lambda$ between the waves received and those emitted.

3. Use data from the graph on page 150 to calculate a value for the Hubble constant.

1. A gaseous element can only emit and absorb certain frequencies or wavelengths. These frequencies or wavelengths are the same for emission and absorption. When white light passes through the gas it absorbs the frequencies in its emission spectrum, leaving dark lines.

2. 0.0033

3. 1.5×10^{-18} s^{-1}

Sample question and model answer

1

Ultrasound is used for examining delicate organs and tissue. The diagram shows how an ultrasound probe is used to examine the retina.

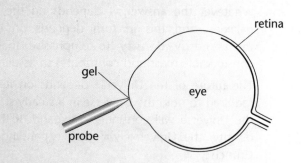

The depth of the eye is 2.5 cm.
The speed of sound in the eye tissue is 1.50×10^3 m s^{-1}.

(a) For the best results, the wavelength used for an ultrasound scan should be 1/200 of the depth of the tissue being scanned.
   Calculate the optimum frequency for scanning a retina. [3]

This is an example of where a question on an extension topic requires recall of material from the core, in this case the wave equations.

optimum wavelength = 1/200 × 2.5 × 10^{-2} m = 1.25 × 10^{-4} m   1 mark
optimum frequency, $f = v/\lambda$ = 1.50 × 10^3 m s^{-1} ÷ 1.25 × 10^{-4} m   1 mark
                                    = 1.20 × 10^7 Hz   1 mark

(b) Explain why the gel is used between the probe and the eyeball. [2]

This is an example of impedance matching to maximise the energy transferred between two materials.

This maximises the energy transmitted into the eye (1 mark) by reducing the amount reflected (1 mark).

(c) In an ultrasound scan a piezoelectric crystal acts as both transmitter and detector of the ultrasound. It emits short pulses of waves, with a time gap between each pulse.

(i) Explain why there is a time gap between each pulse of waves. [2]

To allow the reflected waves to return to the crystal and be detected (1 mark) without interfering with the waves emitted by the crystal. 1 mark

(ii) Estimate the minimum time gap that should be left between pulses in this example. [3]

The minimum time should be that taken for the pulse to travel to the retina and for the reflection to be detected.   1 mark

The factor of two is needed here because the pulse has to travel to the back of the eye and return.

time = distance ÷ speed = 2 × 2.50 × 10^{-2} m ÷ 1.50 × 10^3 m s^{-1} 1 mark
                                    = 3.33 × 10^{-5} s   1 mark

Sample question and model answer *(continued)*

2

(a) Explain the meaning of the *Doppler Effect* and describe, in outline, how it is used to measure the speeds of stars relative to the Earth. [4]

An outline description means that you should describe the physical principles without going into great detail of how the measurements are made.

The Doppler Effect refers to the change in wavelength and frequency when a source of waves is moving relative to an observer (1 mark). The wavelength is increased when the source is moving away from the observer and there is a decrease in wavelength when it moves towards the observer (1 mark).

The faster a star is moving, the greater the change in wavelength (1 mark). To measure the speed of a star, the wavelength received is compared to that emitted by a stationary source (1 mark).

(b) Measurements of *red shift* often show different values for different stars in the same galaxy. Suggest a reason for this.

The effect of the rotation of stars within a galaxy is to broaden the spectral lines received from the galaxy as a whole, showing that stars are moving with a range of speeds relative to the Earth.

Stars within a galaxy are rotating around the centre of the galaxy (1 mark). Depending on the direction of movement of a particular star, this can cause an increase or a decrease in its velocity relative to the Earth and consequently an increase or decrease in the amount of red shift (1 mark).

(c) In the light from a star, the wavelength of a hydrogen line in its absorption spectrum is measured to be 5.153×10^{-7} m. A laboratory measurement of the same spectral line gives its wavelength as 4.861×10^{-7} m.

(i) Calculate the speed of movement of the star relative to the Earth.
$c = 3.00 \times 10^8$ m s^{-1} [2]

There is no mark for the recall of this relationship as it will be given in the question or on a separate data sheet.

$\Delta\lambda/\lambda = v/c$
$v = c \times \Delta\lambda/\lambda = 3.00 \times 10^8$ m s^{-1} $\times (5.153 \times 10^{-7} - 4.861 \times 10^{-7}$ m$)/$ 4.861×10^{-7} m (1 mark) $= 1.80 \times 10^7$ m s^{-1} (1 mark)

(ii) Explain whether the star is moving towards or away from the Earth. [2]

The cue word explain here means that you must give a reason to justify your answer to gain full marks.

The star is moving away from the Earth (1 mark) as the wavelength of light received is greater than that emitted (1 mark).

Practice examination questions

Throughout this section use the following values of the electronic charge and Planck's constant:

$e = -1.60 \times 10^{-19}$ C

$h = 6.63 \times 10^{-34}$ J s

1

Sound is attenuated as it travels in the air.

(a) Explain the meaning of *attenuation*. [1]

(b) Sound from a loudspeaker has an intensity of 6.0×10^{-5} W m^{-2}, measured at a distance of 1 m from the loudspeaker.
The threshold of hearing is 1.0×10^{-12} W m^{-2}.

   (i) Calculate the intensity of the sound at a distance of 1 m from the loudspeaker in decibels. [3]

   (ii) Assuming that the sound is radiated in all directions, calculate the distance from the loudspeaker where the sound becomes inaudible. [3]

   (iii) What is the intensity, in dB, of a sound at the threshold of hearing? [1]

(c) The ear is most sensitive to sounds with a frequency around 3000 Hz.
Explain how the perceived loudness of sounds of equal intensity depends on their frequency. [3]

2

For ultra-sound scanning, a piezoelectric crystal produces a series of pulses of ultrasound and then detects the reflections.

An ultrasound scan is used to detect a tumour at a depth of 6.0 cm below the surface of the skin. The speed of sound in tissue is 1500 m s^{-1}.

(a) Explain whether an A-scan or B-scan is appropriate for this application. [2]

(b) Calculate the time that elapses between the pulse being sent and the echo being detected. [2]

(c) Explain why it is necessary to use a short pulse of ultrasound. [2]

(d) Explain why it is necessary to use pulses of ultrasound rather than a continuous wave. [2]

(e) The optimum frequency is one that produces a wave with a wavelength that is 1/200 the depth of the organ.
Calculate the optimum frequency for this application. [3]

(f) Before a scan is carried out, the skin of the patient is coated with a gel.
Explain the purpose of this gel. [2]

(g) CAT scans are also used to detect tumours.

   (i) Outline the principle of operation of a CAT-scanner. [3]

   (ii) Describe the advantages and disadvantages of using a CAT scan rather than an ultrasound scan to detect a tumour. [3]

3

(a) (i) Explain the meaning of the terms *apparent magnitude* and *absolute magnitude*. [2]

  (ii) Explain why the absolute magnitude is preferred to the apparent magnitude when comparing the magnitudes of stars. [2]

(b) Sirius is at a distance of 2.7 pc from the Earth. Its apparent magnitude is –1.5. Calculate the absolute magnitude of Sirius. [2]

(c) The absolute magnitude of the Pole star is –4.9. Its apparent magnitude is 2.0. Calculate the distance of the Pole Star from the Earth. [2]

(d) White dwarfs are hotter than red giants, but they are less bright. Suggest a reason for this. [2]

4

The hydrogen absorption spectrum contains a dark line corresponding to a wavelength of 6.563×10^{-7} m.

(a) Explain why the lines in an absorption spectrum are dark. [3]

(b) In the spectrum detected from a star, this line has a wavelength of 6.840×10^{-7} m.

  (i) Explain this apparent increase in wavelength. [2]

  (ii) Calculate the speed of the star relative to the Earth. $c = 3.00 \times 10^8$ m s^{-1}. [3]

  (iii) The value of the Hubble constant, $H_0 = (2.12 \times 10^{-18} \pm 0.07)$ s^{-1}. Calculate the range of distances from the Earth within which the star lies. [3]

5

The diagram shows three possible ways in which the size of the Universe could change in the future.

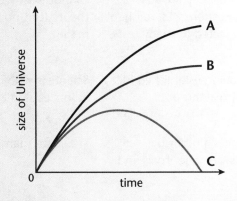

With reference to the graph, explain how the future of the Universe depends on the amount of mass that it contains. [6]

Chapter 5
Synthesis and How Science Works

5.1 How Science Works

You will also be assessed on your understanding of How Science Works. This includes awareness of the following points, shown here with examples or additional explanation.

HOW SCIENCE WORKS	EXAMPLE OR EXPANSION
Observation is at the centre of how science works.	Science studies the observable world and does not study what cannot be directly or indirectly observed.
New ideas and new observations are debated amongst scientists.	The discovery of a global layer of dust made 65 million years ago and a large crater of the same age provides evidence for a major event that could have made the dinosaurs extinct. Many scientists, however, say that more evidence is needed before becoming confident that the event killed the dinosaurs.
Theories that are supported by replicated observations may become accepted as the best available sources of explanations.	There have been very many observations that have supported the idea that atoms exist.
Scientific knowledge can be supported but not proved by observations.	No human observation is ever ABSOLUTELY reliable. Many observations, however, add together to become convincing.
The best available sources of explanations become 'established' scientific ideas, but they are still subject to tests by more observations. 'Established' scientific ideas have been subjected to many tests, and never proved wrong.	Any one observation that showed that atoms cannot exist would be enough to destroy atomic theory (but no such observation has yet been made).
Scientists who succeed in proving established ideas to be wrong make scientific breakthroughs.	Scientists who carry out an experiment that shows atoms couldn't exist would become famous.
Scientists communicate with each other by publishing accounts of their work in journals and by attending conferences.	There are many scientific journals.
Journals are available to the general public, though often only scientists and specialist journalists can understand them.	Journalists look for 'stories' that non-scientists will find particularly interesting.
In order for work to be published it must be reviewed by other scientists to see if it meets required standards of methods and conclusions.	This is called peer review.

HOW SCIENCE WORKS	EXAMPLE OR EXPANSION
Scientific knowledge has a direct impact on how people in general see the world.	The idea that the Earth is not the centre of the Universe (the Copernican revolution) changed the way we see ourselves. Images of the Earth taken from the Moon reinforced this change. We tend to be less conscious of such profound cultural changes than we are of shorter-term changes in fashion.
Scientific knowledge can make new technologies possible.	Experiments on electromagnetism made generation of electricity possible. Experiments on electric circuits and on materials made transistors possible, leading to computer technology.
New technologies can change the way people live and think.	Such technologies include: • Electromagnetism and electricity generation – allowing our nights to be lit up and allowing many labour-saving devices, helping to reduce poverty but also helping to produce pollution in general and climate change in particular • Electromagnetic radiation and communication technology – TV and radio • Mobile telephones – these have made big changes in business and social life • New technologies provide new models and metaphors. People sometimes compare the human brain to a computer, for example.
New technologies often have ethical implications.	There is uncertainty about the safety of mobile phones, especially to children. New technologies make new weapons possible. New technologies raise questions about spending money, especially on healthcare equipment such as MRI scanners.
There may be ethical considerations involved in deciding whether particular scientific research should be done.	Animal experimentation, work on human cells (especially fertilised embryos), work that could lead to new weapons of mass destruction.

5.2 Synoptic assessment

All specifications must include some 'synoptic' assessment at A2. These are questions that require you to bring ideas together from different physics topics. It favours people who really know their physics and who can make links and spot patterns. This chapter provides several themes of physics that will help you to do this.

Themes of physics – energy

Many kinds of system can store energy. A stretched spring and a charged capacitor may not look very similar, but they are both energy storage systems. The formulae for the amount of energy stored are not that different.

For the stretched spring:

$$\text{energy stored} = \text{average applied force} \times \text{extension}$$
$$= \tfrac{1}{2} Fx$$

For the charged capacitor:

$$\text{energy stored} = \text{average applied potential difference} \times \text{charge stored}$$
$$= \tfrac{1}{2} VQ$$

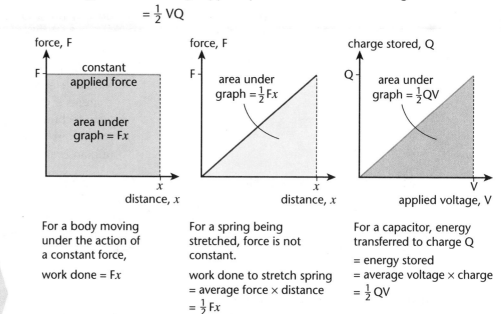

For a body moving under the action of a constant force,

work done = Fx

For a spring being stretched, force is not constant.

work done to stretch spring
= average force × distance
= $\tfrac{1}{2} Fx$

For a capacitor, energy transferred to charge Q

= energy stored
= average voltage × charge
= $\tfrac{1}{2} QV$

> Write down the names of as many energy storage systems as you can think of. Wherever possible, write down a formula that can be used to predict the amount of energy stored by the system.

> Try to think of processes of energy transfer from system to system that do not involve either heating or (even if at a particle level) doing work.

Energy transfers from one kind of source to another, by processes of working and/or heating. Some energy may become thinly spread in the wider environment, or dissipated, but total energy before the process is always the same as total energy after.

This equation is useful for solving problems and making predictions in many areas of physics:

$$\text{total energy before} = \text{total energy after}$$

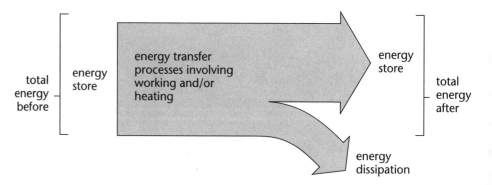

Themes of physics – rates of change with time

The world is not static and if we want to study its changes, we quickly find that it is useful to know about how quickly the changes take place. We study rates of change in many systems.

Displacement, velocity and acceleration

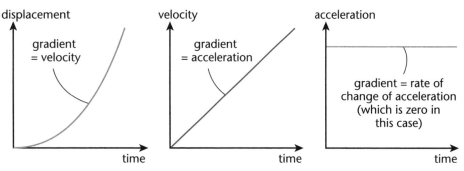

Displacement, velocity and acceleration for a motion that starts from rest and has uniform acceleration

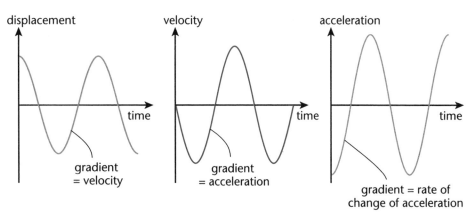

Displacement, velocity and acceleration for a simple harmonic motion with initial displacement equal to the amplitude of the motion.

Energy and power

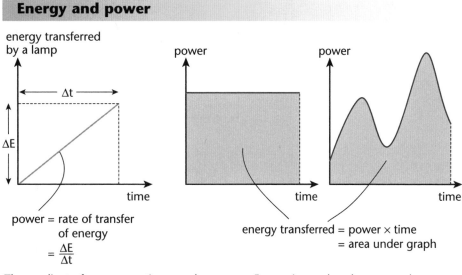

The gradient of an energy–time graph is equal to power. In this case the power is constant (as it is, for example, for an ordinary lamp).

Energy is equal to the area under a power–time graph, whatever the shape of the graph.

Proportionality and exponential rates of change

There are many possible relationships between variables. A simple one is proportionality.

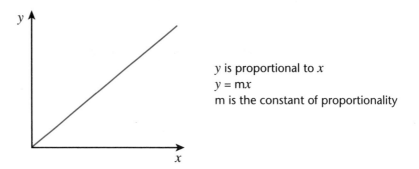

y is proportional to x

$y = mx$

m is the constant of proportionality

Quite often the rate of change of a quantity depends on the size of the quantity itself. That is, there is a relationship between the quantity, x, and its rate of change, $\Delta x / \Delta t$. Sometimes the relationship is simple – the rate of change of x is proportional to x.

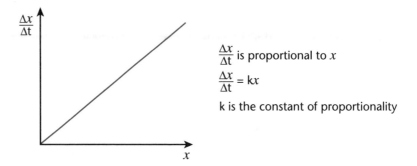

$\dfrac{\Delta x}{\Delta t}$ is proportional to x

$\dfrac{\Delta x}{\Delta t} = kx$

k is the constant of proportionality

This simple relationship always leads to an exponential relationship between the quantity, x, and the time, t.

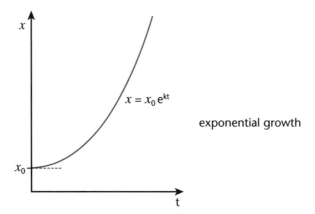

$x = x_0 e^{kt}$

exponential growth

If the constant of proportionality is negative:

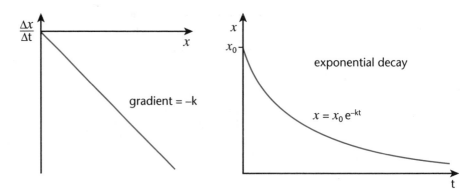

gradient = $-k$

exponential decay

$x = x_0 e^{-kt}$

Themes of physics – rates of change with distance

Temperature gradient

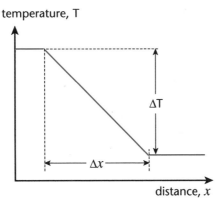

Δx is the thickness of material

ΔT is the temperature difference across the material

Temperature gradient $= \dfrac{\Delta T}{\Delta x}$

Note that rate of transfer of energy through a material depends on the temperature gradient:

Rate of energy transfer, $\dfrac{\Delta Q}{\Delta t} = k\, A\, \dfrac{\Delta T}{\Delta x}$

where k is the thermal conductivity of the material and A is its cross-sectional area.

Potential gradient

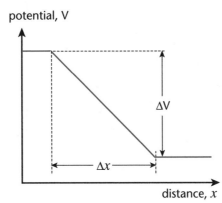

Δx is the length of the resistor

ΔV is the potential difference across the resistor

Potential gradient $= \dfrac{\Delta V}{\Delta x}$

Note that rate of transfer of charge (electric current) through a resistor depends on the potential gradient:

Rate of transfer of charge = current, $I = \dfrac{\Delta Q}{\Delta t} = \sigma\, A\, \dfrac{\Delta V}{\Delta x}$

where σ is the electrical conductivity of the resisting material and A is its cross-sectional area.

Pressure gradient

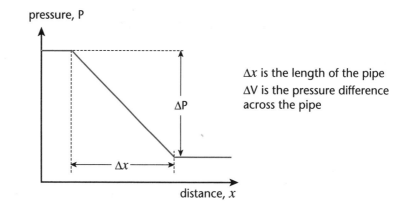

Δx is the length of the pipe
ΔV is the pressure difference across the pipe

$$\text{Pressure gradient} = \frac{\Delta P}{\Delta x}$$

Note that rate of transfer of liquid through a pipe depends on the pressure gradient:

$$\text{Rate of transfer of liquid} = \frac{\Delta m}{\Delta t} = c\,A\,\frac{\Delta P}{\Delta x}$$

where m is the mass of liquid, c is a constant that depends on the properties of the liquid, and A is the cross-sectional area of the pipe.

The inverse square law

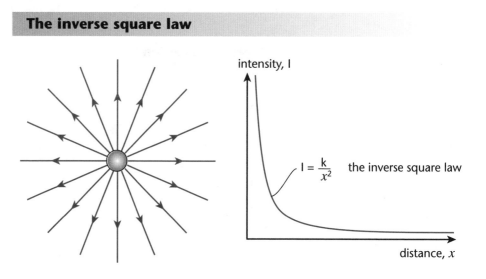

$I = \dfrac{k}{x^2}$ the inverse square law

Any situation that involves intensity that radiates from a point into three dimensions also involves an inverse square law of intensity.

The 'intensity' can be intensity of field lines in an electric or gravitational field, or it can be intensity of electromagnetic radiation emitted by a point source.

Exponential decrease with distance

Consider a parallel (that is, non-spreading) beam of radiation that travels from a non-absorbing medium across a boundary into an absorbing material.

The rate of absorption is proportional to the beam intensity. So the intensity decreases exponentially with distance:

$$I = I_0\, e^{-cx}$$

The value of x that corresponds with beam intensity that is half of the initial value is called half-value thickness, $x_{\frac{1}{2}}$.

The mathematics of half-value thickness is similar to that of half-life of radioactive decay.

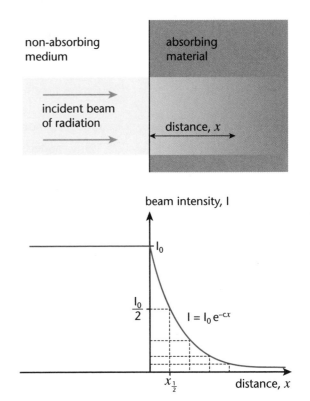

Themes of physics – predictions, models and simplifications

Physics predicts the future. Formulae provide predictive answers. To take a simple example, knowing the length of a journey and an expected average speed, it is possible to calculate the expected journey time. Or, knowing the weight to be supported by a cable it is possible to predict, by calculation, the thickness of cable needed. Meteorology is a branch of physics, and weather forecasters must use complex formulae to make predictions of the complex behaviour of weather systems. They combine their formulae into a computer model – a simulation of the weather.

A model is something that behaves like something else, without BEING the something else. A simple formula is a kind of simple model – it copies the behaviour that is actually observable in the 'real' world. A computer model is just a sophisticated version.

There are visual models, too. A map is a predictive model of the landscape, made so that a person can know what is over the next hill before they ever see it. There are models of atoms – many different models, in fact.

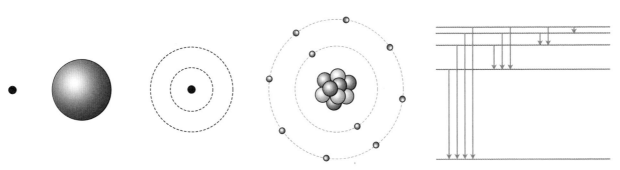

Different models of atoms used for making predictions of behaviour in different circumstances

Each of the above models predicts different aspects of the behaviour of atoms. A trained scientist will use the best model to match the required predictions.

A test of a model is not whether or not it is absolutely correct, but whether it gives good predictions. That means that models have to be used carefully – different models of the same real systems are useful in different circumstances, so that the skill of using the right model is an important one, and quite hard to learn.

A scientific theory is more than a model. An established scientific theory is the best available system of interpretation of observations. So a scientist can move from model to model freely, but will work within just one theory.

Many models use simplifications. Think of the light around you now. It is spreading from a source, or sources. It is reflecting from surfaces. Some of the light passes through the pupils of your eyes, and helps you know and learn about the world so that you can predict its behaviour. Most of the light misses your pupils. You are immersed in a sea of light that you will never see. But physicists interpret light using just simple straight lines drawn on paper – rays of light. It is almost absurdly simple, compared with the real sea of light, but it is very good at producing valuable predictions.

Newton's ideas about force and motion still have huge predictive ability, and so they remain on your exam specifications. But they make assumptions about space as a framework in which events take place and about time as absolute and universal. These assumptions have been shown, by ideas of relativity, to be false. Newtonian ideas cannot explain behaviour of very fast motion, nor gravitational lensing of light from very distant sources. They do not provide the best possible source of explanations of all of our observations. As scientific theory, they have failed, but as predictive models their importance lives on. It is just necessary to remember not to use them as predictive models in more extreme situations, such as when considering the motions of particles in accelerators or the travel of light around massive objects like black holes.

Rays of light are extremely simple compared with the reality of light, but they are also extremely useful for predicting the behaviour of light

Sample questions and model answers

1

The gravitational field due to a point mass and the electric field due to a point positive charge show some similarities and differences.

One similarity is that both follow inverse square laws.

> The definitions of gravitational and electric field strength are 'force per unit mass' and 'force per unit positive charge'.

(a) (i) Write down expressions for the gravitational field strength due to a point mass, *m*, and the electric field strength due to a point positive charge, q. [2]

$g = Gm/r^2$ 1 mark
$E = q/4\pi\varepsilon_0 r^2$ 1 mark

> All radial fields follow inverse square laws.

(ii) What feature of these expressions shows that the fields follow an inverse square law? [1]

The r^2 term in the denominator shows that the field strengths vary as the inverse of the square of the distance from the mass or charge.   1 mark

(iii) State one other way in which the definitions of gravitational field strength and electric field strength are similar. [1]

They are both proportional to the size of the mass or charge.   1 mark

(iv) State one way in which the definitions of gravitational field strength and electric field strength are different. [2]

> A negative charge experiences a force the same size as that experienced by a positive charge, but in the opposite direction.

The definition of gravitational field strength does not specify the sign of the mass as mass can only have positive values.   1 mark
The definition of electric field strength specifies that it is the size of the force on a positive charge.   1 mark

(b) Gravitational potential and electric potential are properties of points within a field.
How is potential related to the potential energy of:

(i) a mass in a gravitational field? [1]

Potential energy = potential x mass.   1 mark

> Potential means 'the energy per unit mass/charge placed at that point'.

(ii) a charge within an electric field? [1]

Potential energy = potential x charge (including the sign of the charge).   1 mark

(c) Explain why the expressions for gravitational potential and electric potential have opposite signs. [4]

Gravitational forces can only be attractive (1 mark) so a point in a gravitational field always has a negative potential since energy would be needed to remove the mass to infinity (1 mark). The direction of an electric field is taken to be the direction of the force on a positive charge (1 mark). A positive charge in the field of another positive charge has a positive amount of energy since work would have to be done on the charge to move it from infinity to a point in the field (1 mark).

2

A motorist sees a bright light in the sky and she first thinks that it is the planet Venus. Then she notices that the movement across the sky is too rapid for a planet and realises that she is looking at a low-flying aircraft.

At its brightest, Venus reflects electromagnetic radiation from the Sun with a power of 2.8×10^{17} W. On this occasion, the distance between Venus and the Earth was 8.0×10^{10} m.

The power of the lights of a large aircraft is 1500 W.

Estimate the distance of the aircraft from the motorist for its lights to appear as bright as Venus. State the assumptions that it is necessary to make and explain whether your answer is likely to be too high or too low. [12]

The marks are awarded here for setting up a workable mathematical model – like the Earth, only half of Venus is receiving radiation from the Sun at any one time.

You are not expected to know that the surface area of a sphere = $4\pi r^2$, this information is given in a data book.

It is important when making an estimate to round off the answer to a sensible number of significant figures.

The reasons for the answer are important here. No marks are awarded for a 50–50 guess.

Assuming that Venus acts as a disc (1 mark) and reflects radiation over a hemisphere (1 mark):

Intensity of light from Venus at the Earth
$= P/2\pi r^2$ ... 1 mark
$= 2.8 \times 10^{17}$ W $\div$ $(2 \times \pi \times (8.0 \times 10^{10}$ m$)^2)$ ... 1 mark
$= 7.0 \times 10^{-6}$ W m^{-2} ... 1 mark

At a distance d, for the aircraft lights to have the same intensity, assuming that they radiate light equally in all directions over a hemisphere ... 1 mark

$P/2\pi r^2 =$ observed intensity

1500 W $\div$ $(2 \times \pi \times d^2) = 7.0 \times 10^{-6}$ W m^{-2} ... 1 mark

$d = \sqrt{(1500 \text{ W} \div (2 \times \pi \times 7.0 \times 10^{-6} \text{ W m}^{-2})}$ ... 1 mark

$= 5.8 \times 10^3$ m or about 6 km ... 1 mark

This is assuming that the light from Venus and the aircraft contains the same proportion of visible radiation. ... 1 mark

If this is the case, then at a distance of 6 km the aircraft is likely to appear brighter than Venus, since its lights are focused into a beam, (1 mark) so I would expect my answer to be too low (1 mark).

Practice examination questions

1

A mass spectrometer is a device for comparing atomic masses. Positive ions pass through slits A and B before entering a region where there is both an electric and a magnetic field.

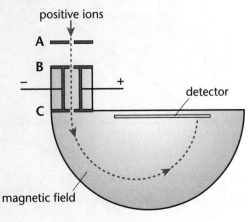

(a) Suggest why the ions must first pass through slits A and B. [1]

(b) State the direction of:
   (i)   the electric force on the ions
   (ii) the magnetic force on the ions
   (iii) the magnetic field. [3]

(c) Show that an ion can only pass through slit C if its velocity is equal to the ratio of the field strengths. [2]

(d) (i) Explain why an ion follows a circular path after leaving slit C. [2]
   (ii) An ion of carbon-12 has a mass of 2.0×10^{-26} kg and carries a single positive charge of 1.6×10^{-19} C. It emerges from slit C with a speed of 2.4×10^{5} m s^{-1}.
   The magnetic field strength is 0.15 T.
   Calculate the radius of its circular path. [3]

(e) Radiocarbon dating is a method of estimating the age of objects made from materials that were once alive. In a living object the ratio of carbon-12 atoms to carbon-14 atoms is 10^{12} to one.
   Suggest how a mass spectrometer could be used to estimate the age of wood from an old table. [3]

2

In a Van de Graaff generator, charge from a moving belt is transferred onto a spherical metal dome which is insulated from the ground.

The graph below shows how the potential of a dome of radius 0.12 m depends on the charge on it.

Practice examination questions *(continued)*

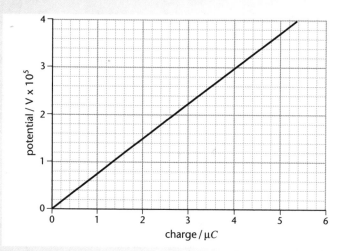

(a) Calculate the capacitance of the dome. [3]

(b) Calculate the amount of work that has to be done to place 4.0 μC of charge on the dome. [3]

The dome loses charge when the electric field strength at its surface reaches a value of 3.0×10^6 N C^{-1}.

(c) (i) Calculate the charge on the dome when the electric field strength at its surface has this value. [3]

$$k = 1/4\pi\varepsilon_0 = 9.0 \times 10^9 \text{ N m}^2 \text{ C}^{-2}$$

(ii) What is the potential of the dome when the electric field strength at its surface has this value? [1]

(d) (i) Calculate the force on an electron, charge = -1.6×10^{-19} C, near the surface of the dome when the electric field strength is 3.0×10^6 N C^{-1}. [3]

(ii) Suggest how the dome loses charge. [3]

3

Read the passage and answer the questions that follow.

Seismometers on the Moon's surface have detected very slight tremors in the body of the Moon. Some of these occur at irregular intervals and appear to originate at the Moon's surface. Others are regular and are repeated on a 14-day cycle. These regular Moonquakes originate deep below the Moon's surface and could be due to tidal stresses caused by the Moon's elliptical orbit.

It is not known whether the Earth undergoes similar tidal stresses, since the small magnitude of the tremors means that they would be indistinguishable from movement caused by other factors.

(a) Suggest one cause of the irregular tremors. [1]

(b) What 'other factors' could cause small Earth tremors? [2]

(c) Here is some data about the Moon and its orbit.

Mass of Moon = 7.4×10^{22} kg
Orbital period = 27.3 days
Closest distance between Moon and Earth = 3.56×10^8 m
Greatest distance between Moon and Earth = 4.06×10^8 m.

Estimate the difference between the greatest and smallest forces that the Earth exerts on the Moon. State clearly any assumptions and approximations that you make and what effect these are likely to have on your answer. [12]

Practice examination answers

1 Mechanics

1 (a) $\Delta E_p = mg\Delta h$ [1] = 40 kg × 10 m s^{-2} × 0.60 m [1] = 240 J [1].
   (b) $\frac{1}{2}mv^2 = 240$ J [1] $v = \sqrt{(2 \times 240 \text{ J} \div 40 \text{ kg})}$ [1] = 3.5 m s^{-1} [1].
   (c) The child is accelerating [1] upwards [1].
   (d) $F = mv^2/r$ [1] = 40 kg × (3.5 m s^{-1})^2 ÷ 3.2 m [1] = 153 N [1].
   (e) The downward gravitational pull [1] of the Earth [1].
   (f) (i) 400 N [1] (ii) 550 N [1].

2 (a) Taking momentum to the right as positive, 0.30 kg m s^{-1} [1] – 0.16 kg m s^{-1} [1] = 0.14 kg m s^{-1} [1].
   (b) 0.14 kg m s^{-1} ÷ 1.00 kg [1] = 0.14 m s^{-1} [1] to the right [1].
   (c) Total kinetic energy before collision = 0.107 J [1].
       Kinetic energy after collision = 9.8 × 10^{-3} J [1].
       The collision is inelastic as there is less kinetic energy after the collision than before [1].

3 (a) $v = 2\pi r/T$ [1] = 2 × π × 4.24 × 10^7 m × (24 h × 60 min h^{-1} × 60 s min^{-1}) [1] = 3.08 × 10^3 m s^{-1} [1].
   (b) Acceleration = v^2/r [1] = (3.08 × 10^3 m s^{-1})^2 ÷ 4.24 × 10^7 m [1] = 0.24 m s^{-2} [1] towards the centre of the Earth [1].
   (c) The gravitational pull [1] of the Earth [1].

4 (a) 0.06 kg × 15 m s^{-1} [1] – – 0.06 kg × 24 m s^{-1} [1] = 2.34 kg m s^{-1} [1].
   (b) Force = rate of change of momentum [1] = 2.34 kg m s^{-1} [1] ÷ 0.012 s [1] = 195 N [1].
   (c) 195 N
   (d) From kinetic energy of the ball and racket [1] to potential energy of the squashed ball and stretched strings [1] and back to kinetic energy of the ball [1].

5 (a) 600 N × cos 20° [1] = 564 N [1].
   (b) Friction between the ground and the log [1]; 564 N [1].
   (c) $W = F \times s$ [1] = 564 N × 250 m [1] = 1.41 × 10^5 J [1].
   (d) It is transferred to the log and the ground [1] as heat [1].

6 (a) v^2/r [1] = (14 m s^{-1})^2 ÷ 100 m [1] = 1.96 m s^{-2} [1].
   (b) $F = ma$ [1] = 800 kg × 1.96 m s^{-2} [1] = 1.57 × 10^3 N [1].
   (c) (i) The frictional push [1] of the road on the tyres [1].
       (ii) The frictional push [1] of the tyres on the road [1].
   (d) Friction between the tyres and the road is reduced [1] and may not be sufficient for the centripetal force required [1].

7 (a) 5.0 × 10^5 kg × 60 m s^{-1} [1] = 3.0 × 10^7 kg m s^{-1} [1].
   (b) 3.0 × 10^7 kg m s^{-1} ÷ 20 s [1] = 1.5 × 10^6 N [1].
   (c) Resistive forces oppose the motion [1] so a greater forwards force is needed to produce this unbalanced force [1].
   (d) The aircraft gains momentum in the forwards direction [1]. The exhaust gases gain an equal amount of momentum in the opposite direction [1].

8 (a) $\Delta E_p = mg\Delta h$ [1] = 3.2 × 10^5 kg × 10 m s^{-2} × 180 m [1] = 5.76 × 10^8 J [1].
   (b) $\frac{1}{2}mv^2 = 5.76 \times 10^8$ J [1] $v = \sqrt{(2 \times 5.76 \times 10^8 \text{ J} \div 3.2 \times 10^5 \text{ kg})}$ [1] = 60 m s^{-1} [1].
   (c) $\frac{1}{2}$ × 3.2 × 10^5 kg × (60 m s^{-1})^2 – $\frac{1}{2}$ × 3.2 × 10^5 kg × (3 m s^{-1})^2 [1] = 5.7 × 10^8 J [1].

9 (a) The frequency an object vibrates at, when it is displaced from its normal position [1] and released [1].

(b) When the frequency of a forcing vibration [1] is equal to the natural frequency [1].

(c) $f = v/\lambda$ [1] = 340 m s^{-1} ÷ 0.15 m [1] = 2.27×10^3 Hz [1].

10 (a) a represents acceleration [1], k represents the spring constant [1], x represents the displacement [1] and m represents the value of the mass [1].

(b) (i) 0.13 m [1].

(ii) $f = 1/T$ [1] = 1 ÷ 1.6 s = 0.625 Hz [1].

(c) $k = 4\pi^2 f^2 m$ [1]

$\quad = 4\pi^2 \times (0.625)^2 \times 0.5$ [1]

$\quad = 7.7$ N m^{-1} [1].

(d) (i) $v_{max} = 2\pi fA = 0.51$ m s^{-1} [1], E_k at this speed = ½ × 0.50 kg × (0.51 m s^{-1})^2 [1] = 6.5×10^{-2} J [1].

(ii) At zero displacement [1].

11 (a) A = 0.28 m [1], f = 0.67 Hz [1].

(b) $v_{max} = 2\pi fA = 1.18$ m s^{-1} [1].

(c) $v = 2\pi f\sqrt{(A^2 - x^2)}$ [1] = 0.82 m s^{-1} [1]

2 Fields

1 (a) $F = kQ_1Q_2/r^2$ [1] = 9.0×10^9 N m^2 C^{-2} × $(1.6 \times 10^{-19}$ C)^2 ÷ $(5.2 \times 10^{-11}$ m)^2 [1] = 8.5×10^{-8} N [1].

(b) (i) $E = kQ/r^2$ [1] = 9.0×10^9 N m^2 C^{-2} × 1.6×10^{-19} C ÷ $(5.2 \times 10^{-11}$ m)^2 [1] = 5.3×10^{11} N C^{-1} [1].

(ii) From the proton towards the electron [1].

(c) $v = \sqrt{(r \times F \div m_e)}$ [1] = $\sqrt{(5.2 \times 10^{-11}}$ m × 8.5×10^{-8} N ÷ 9.1×10^{-31} kg) [1] = 2.2×10^6 m s^{-1} [1].

2 (a) (i) 1250 V [1]

(ii) $E = qV$ [1] = 10 × 1.6×10^{-19} C × 1250 V [1] = 2.0×10^{-15} J [1].

(b) 4.0×10^{-15} J [1].

(c) (i) Top plate positive and lower plate negative [1].

(ii) $Vq/d = mg$ [1] $V = mgd/q = 5.0 \times 10^{-5}$ kg × 10.0 m s^{-2} × 6.0×10^{-3} m ÷ 1.6×10^{-18} C [1] = 1.9×10^{12} V [1].

3 (a) (i) $g = GM_E/r^2$ [1] = 6.7×10^{-11} N m^2 kg^{-2} × 6.0×10^{24} kg ÷ $(3.8 \times 10^8$ m)^2 [1] = 2.8×10^{-3} N kg^{-1} [1].

(ii) 2.8×10^{-3} N kg^{-1} × 7.4×10^{21} kg [1] = 2.1×10^{19} N [1].

(iii) $T = 2\pi\sqrt{(rM_M/F)}$ [1] = $2\pi\sqrt{(3.8 \times 10^8}$ m × 7.4×10^{21} kg ÷ 2.1×10^{19} N) [1] = 2.3×10^6 s [1].

(b) (i) $F = GMm/r^2$ [1] = 6.7×10^{-11} N m^2 kg^{-2} × 7.4×10^{21} kg × 1.0 kg ÷ $(3.8 \times 10^8$ m)^2 [1] = 3.4×10^{-6} N [1].

(ii) The Sun has a greater mass than the Moon [1] but it is very much further away from the Earth [1] so its gravitational field strength at the surface of the Earth is less [1].

(iii) In position A the gravitational pulls of the Moon and the Sun are in the same direction [1], in position B they are in opposite directions, so the resultant force on the water is smaller [1].

4 (a) From N to S (radially outwards) [1].
   (b) Out of the paper [1].
   (c) The direction of the force on the electromagnet reverses [1] when the current reverses direction [1].
   (d) $F = BIl = BI2\pi rN$ [1] $= 0.85\,T \times 0.055\,A \times 2 \times \pi \times 2.5 \times 10^{-2}\,m \times 150$ [1] $= 1.1\,N$ [1].

5 (a) (i) $E_k = eV$ [1] $= 1.6 \times 10^{-19}\,C \times 2500\,V$ [1] $= 4.0 \times 10^{-16}\,J$ [1].
      (ii) $v = \sqrt{(2E_k/m)}$ [1] $= \sqrt{(2 \times 4.0 \times 10^{-16}\,J \div 9.1 \times 10^{-31}\,kg)}$ [1] $= 3.0 \times 10^7\,m\,s^{-1}$ [1].
   (b) (i) Down (from top to bottom of the paper) [1].
      (ii) There is an unbalanced force on the electrons [1] which is always at right angles to the direction of motion [1].
      (iii) $r = mv/Bq$ [1] $= 9.1 \times 10^{-31}\,kg \times 3.0 \times 10^7\,m\,s^{-1} \div (2.0 \times 10^{-3}\,T \times 1.6 \times 10^{-19}\,C)$ [1] $= 8.5 \times 10^{-2}\,m$

6 (a) (i) $\phi = BA$ [1] $= 0.15\,T \times 8.0 \times 10^{-2}\,m \times 5.0 \times 10^{-2}\,m$ [1] $= 6.0 \times 10^{-4}\,Wb$ [1].
      (ii) 0 [1].
   (b) (i) The reading is a maximum when the plane of the coil passes through the vertical position [1] as the rate of change of flux is greatest [1]. The reading decreases to zero when the plane of the coil is horizontal [1] as the rate of change of flux decreases to zero [1].
      (ii) Generator/dynamo [1].
   (c) Any three from: increase the speed of rotation, increase the number of turns on the coil, increase the area of the coil, increase the strength of the magnetic field [1 mark each].

3 Thermal and particle physics

1 (a) (i) A temperature difference of 10 K can be measured more precisely than one of 1 K [1]
      (ii) There is less energy loss to the surroundings [1]
      (iii) The energy supplied heats the block and replaces the energy lost to the surroundings [1] so this should give a higher value [1]
      (iv) Insulate the block to reduce energy losses [1].
   (b) $c = E/m\Delta\theta$ [1] $= 24\,W \times 350\,s \div (0.80\,kg \times 14\,K)$ [1] $= 750\,J\,kg^{-1}\,K^{-1}$ [1].

2 (a) ΔU is the increase in internal energy [1]
      Q is the heat supplied to the gas [1]
      W is the work done on the gas [1].
   (b) The temperature drops [1] as the heat removed from the gas is greater than the work done on it [1].

3 (a) Efficiency = useful power output ÷ power input = 2 kW ÷ 8 kW [1] = 0.25 [1].
   (b) $(T_H - T_C) \div T_H = (1023\,K - 423\,K) \div 1023\,K$ [1] $= 0.59$ [1].
   (c) Some energy is wasted as heat [1].

4 (a) 25 + 273 = 298 K [1]
  (b) pV = nRT

  $n = \frac{pV}{RT}$ [1] = $\frac{2.02 \times 10^5 \times 2.2 \times 10^{-6}}{8.3 \times 298}$ [1] =

  (c) (i) The total kinetic and potential energy of its particles [1]
    (ii) Kinetic energy [1]
    (iii) It doubles [1], internal energy of an ideal gas is proportional to temperature [1]
    (iv) pV = nRT and since p, n and R all remain the same the volume doubles when the temperature does [1]. New volume is 4.40×10^{-6} m³ [1].

5 (a) (i) $^{239}_{92}$U [1]
    (ii) the nucleus is unstable [1] it splits into two smaller nuclei [1] and a small number of free neutrons [1]
    (iii) the free neutrons from any previous fission [1] can combine with more nuclei (of $^{239}_{92}$U) and induce fission [1]
  (b) (i) Binding energy per nucleon increases [1]
    Mass of particles decreases [1]
    (ii) Kinetic energy [1] of the fission products [1]
    (iii) (Primary) coolant carries energy away from the reaction [1]
    This heats steam [1]
    The steam turns turbines [1]
  (c) (i) absorb neutrons [1]
    (ii) slows neutrons down [1]

6 (a) 295 K [1].
  (b) $n = \frac{pV}{RT}$ [1] = $\frac{(1.2 \times 10^5 \times 1.5 \times 10^{-4})}{8.3 \times 295}$ [1] = 7.4×10^{-3} [1].

  (c) $\frac{P_1}{T_1} = \frac{P_2}{T_2}$

  $T_2 = \frac{P_2 T_1}{P_1}$ [1]

  $= \frac{(2 \times 10^5 \times 295)}{1.2 \times 10^5}$ [1]

  = 491.7 K [1].

  (d) (i) mean kinetic energy = $\frac{3}{2}$ kT [1]

    $= \frac{(3 \times 1.38 \times 10^{-23} \times 295)}{2}$

    $= 6.1 \times 10^{-21}$ J [1]
    (ii) 590 K [1], temperature in Kelvin has doubled, mean kinetic energy is proportional to Kelvin temperature [1]

7 $\Delta E = m L + m c \Delta T$ [1]
  $= 1.8 \times 2.25 \times 10^6 + 1.8 \times 4.2 \times 10^3 \times 15$ [1]
  $= 4.16 \times 10^6$ J [1]

8 (a) $t = mc\Delta\theta/P$ [1] = 1.50 kg × 4.2×10^3 J kg⁻¹ K⁻¹ × 90 K ÷ 2.40×10^3 W [1] = 236 s [1].
  (b) The element absorbs energy [1], the casing absorbs energy [1], energy is lost through conduction/convection/evaporation/radiation [1].

9 (a) Gamma [1], gamma can penetrate tissue but beta is absorbed by tissue [1].
(b) The beta radiation emitted by iodine-131 is absorbed and causes ionisation [1], resulting in the damage of cells/tissue [1].
(c) Iodine-123 has a shorter half-life [1] so less is needed to produce the same rate of decay [1].
(d) After 6 half-lives [1] = 78 hours [1].

10 (a) (i) Electrons are not repelled by the nucleus [1]. They have wave-like behaviour so are diffracted by a nucleus [1].
(ii) The higher the energy, the shorter the wavelength [1]. The wavelength needs to be short so that it is of the order of the size of a nucleus [1] for diffraction to occur [1].
(b) (i) $R = 1.20 \times 10^{-15}$ m $\times 4^{1/3}$ [1] $= 1.90 \times 10^{-15}$ m [1].
(ii) 3.81×10^{-15} m [1].
(c) The densities are the same [1]. The radius of the sulphur nucleus is twice that of the helium nucleus [1] so its mass should be $2^3 = 8$ times as great if it has the same density, which it is [1].

11 (a) This shows that most alpha particles do not go close to a region of charge [1], so most of the volume of an atom is empty space [1].
(b) There is a tiny concentration of charge in the atom [1] which must be the same charge as the alpha particles [1] to repel them [1]

12 (a) (i) hf is the energy of a photon [1], Φ is the work function, i.e. minimum photon energy that causes emission [1] and $(\frac{1}{2}mv^2)_{max}$ is the maximum amount of kinetic energy of an emitted electron.
(ii) Some electrons need more than the minimum energy to liberate them, so they have less than the maximum kinetic energy [1].
(b) (i) $E = hf = 2.02 \times 10^{15}$ Hz $\times 6.63 \times 10^{-34}$ J s [1] $= 1.34 \times 10^{-18}$ J [1].
(ii) 4.5×10^{-6} W m$^{-2} \times 2.5 \times 10^{-6}$ m$^2 \div 1.34 \times 10^{-18}$ J [1] $= 8.40 \times 10^6$ [1].
(iii) $hf - (\frac{1}{2}mv^2)_{max}$ [1] $= 1.34 \times 10^{-18}$ J $- 4.05 \times 10^{-19}$ J $= 9.35 \times 10^{-19}$ J [1] $\div 1.60 \times 10^{-19}$ J eV$^{-1} = 5.8$ eV [1].

4 Further physics

1 (a) The intensity decreases [1].
(b) (i) Intensity $= 10 \log (I/I_0)$ [1] $= 10 \log (6.0 \times 10^{-5}$ W m$^{-2} \div 1.0 \times 10^{-12}$ W m$^{-2})$ [1] $= 78$ dB [1].
(ii) $r_0 = \sqrt{r_i^2(I/I_0)}$ [1] $= \sqrt{(6.0 \times 10^{-5}$ W m$^{-2} \div 1.0 \times 10^{-12}$ W m$^{-2})}$ [1] $= 7.7 \times 10^3$ m [1].
(iii) 0 [1].
(c) The perceived loudness of a sound is greatest at a frequency of 3000 Hz [1]. It decreases [1] as the frequency becomes lower or higher [1].

2 (a) An A-scan [1] as this measures depth below the surface of the skin [1].

(b) t = 2 × s ÷ v [1] = 0.12 m ÷ 1500 m s⁻¹ = 8.0 × 10⁻⁵ s [1].

(c) So that there is no interference [1] between the pulse and its reflection [1].

(d) There needs to be a time lag when the crystal is not emitting ultrasound [1] so that it can detect the reflection [1].

(e) λ = 6.0 × 10⁻² m ÷ 200 = 3.0 × 10⁻⁴ m [1]; f = v/λ = 1500 m s⁻¹ ÷ 3.0 × 10⁻⁴ m [1] = 5.0 × 10⁶ Hz [1].

(f) The gel maximises the energy transmitted into the body [1] by reducing the amount that is reflected [1].

(g) (i) A CAT-scanner uses an X-ray beam [1] that rotates around the body [1] and produces a three-dimensional image of the body [1].

(ii) Advantages: the CAT-scan produces a three-dimensional image [1], tumours are more easily detected [1]. Disadvantage: X-rays can be more damaging to body cells and tissue [1].

3 (a) (i) Apparent magnitude is a measure of the brightness when viewed from the Earth [1].

Absolute magnitude is the apparent magnitude the star would have at a distance of 10 pc [1].

(ii) The perceived brightness of a star decreases with increasing distance [1]. Absolute magnitude takes account of this [1].

(b) M = m − 5 log (d/10) [1] = 1.3 [1].

(c) d = 10 log⁻¹ (m−M)/5 [1] = 240 pc [1].

(d) White dwarfs are smaller than red giants [1] so radiation is emitted from less surface area [1].

4 (a) An absorption spectrum is what remains of the full spectrum after passing through an element [1]. Elements absorb the same wavelengths as they emit [1] so the absorption spectrum has these wavelengths removed from the full spectrum, leaving dark lines [1].

(b) (i) The star is moving away from the Earth [1], causing the wavelengths received to be longer than those emitted [1].

(ii) v = cΔλ/λ [1] = 3.00 × 10⁸ m s⁻¹ × (0.277 ÷ 6.563) [1] = 1.27 × 10⁷ m s⁻¹ [1].

(iii) d = v/H [1] = 5.78 × 10²⁴ m [1] to 6.18 × 10²⁴ m [1].

5 A shows an open Universe [1], the Universe will continue to expand if there is insufficient mass for gravitational forces to stop this [1].

B shows a steady-state [1] where the expansion stops due to gravitational attraction of the mass in the Universe, for this to happen the Universe needs to have the critical mass [1].

C shows the Universe contracting to a 'Big Crunch' [1], this will only happen if the mass of the Universe is greater than the critical mass [1]

5 Synthesis and How Science Works

1 (a) To produce a parallel beam [1].
  (b) (i) from right to left [1]
    (ii) from left to right [1]
    (iii) into the paper [1].
  (c) To move in a straight line, $Bqv = Eq$ [1] so $v = E/B$ [1].
  (d) (i) The only force acting is the magnetic force [1], this is always at right angles to the direction of motion [1].
    (ii) $r = mv/Bq$ [1] $= 2.0 \times 10^{-26}$ kg $\times 2.4 \times 10^5$ m s^{-1} $\div (0.15$ T $\times 1.6 \times 10^{-19}$ C) [1] $= 0.20$ m [1].
  (e) The ratio of carbon-14 atoms to carbon-12 atoms decreases after a tree is felled. Use a sample of carbon from the wood in the table in the spectrometer; the carbon-14 atoms follow a path with a greater radius of curvature than that of the carbon-12 atoms [1]. The ratio of carbon-14 to carbon-12 can be determined by using counters [1].

2 (a) $C = Q/V$ [1] $= 4.8 \times 10^{-6}$ C $\div 3.6 \times 10^5$ V [1] $= 1.33 \times 10^{-11}$ F [1].
  (b) $W = \frac{1}{2}QV$ [1] $= \frac{1}{2} \times 4.0 \times 10^{-6}$ C $\times 3.0 \times 10^5$ V [1] $= 0.60$ J [1].
  (c) (i) $Q = Er^2/k$ [1] $= 3.0 \times 10^6$ N C^{-1} $\times (0.12$ m$)^2$ $\div 9.0 \times 10^9$ N m^2 C^{-2} [1] $= 4.8 \times 10^{-6}$ C [1].
    (ii) $V = kQ/r = Er$ [1] $= 3.0 \times 10^6$ N V^{-1} $\times 0.12$ m [1] $= 3.6 \times 10^5$ V [1].
  (d) (i) $F = Eq$ [1] $= 3.0 \times 10^6$ N C^{-1} $\times 1.6 \times 10^{-19}$ C [1] $= 4.8 \times 10^{-13}$ N [1].
    (ii) The force on the outer electrons ionises the air [1], movement of these ions causes further ionisation [1], the dome discharges as it attracts ions of the opposite charge to it [1].

3 (a) Collisions with meteors [1].
  (b) Any two from traffic, wind, tides [2].
  (c) The mean speed of the Moon is calculated by assuming that the path is circular [1] with a mean radius of 3.81×10^8 m [1].
    mean speed $= (2 \times \pi \times 3.81 \times 10^8$ m$) \div (27.3 \times 24 \times 60 \times 60$ s$)$ [1]
      $= 1.01 \times 10^3$ m s^{-1} [1].
    The gravitational force between the Moon and the Sun is the centripetal force [1].
    Force at closest distance $= mv^2/r$ [1]
      $= 7.4 \times 10^{22}$ kg $\times (1.01 \times 10^3$ m s$^{-1})^2 \div (3.56 \times 10^8$ m) [1]
      $= 2.12 \times 10^{20}$ N [1]
    Force at greatest distance $= 1.88 \times 10^{20}$ N [1].
    The difference between these forces $= 2.4 \times 10^{19}$ N.

    The actual difference is likely to be greater than this because of the assumption that the Moon travels at a constant speed [1]. In fact it speeds up as it gets closer to the Earth and slows down as it moves further away [1]. The effect of this would be to make the largest force larger and the smallest force smaller [1].

Index